International Union of Pure and Applied Chemistry

Drugs in Competitive Athletics

Proceedings of the First International Symposium held on
the Islands of Brioni, Yugoslavia 29 May – 2 June 1988

EDITED BY

JAMES R. SHIPE Jr & JOHN SAVORY
Both of University of Virginia Health Sciences Center, USA

OXFORD

Blackwell Scientific Publications

LONDON EDINBURGH BOSTON

MELBOURNE PARIS BERLIN VIENNA

© 1991 International Union of Pure and
Applied Chemistry and published for them by
Blackwell Scientific Publications
Editorial Offices:
Osney Mead, Oxford OX2 0EL
25 John Street, London WC1N 2BL
23 Ainslie Place, Edinburgh EH3 6AJ
3 Cambridge Center, Cambridge
   Massachusetts 02142, USA
54 University Street, Carlton
   Victoria 3053, Australia

Other Editorial Offices:
Arnette SA, 2, rue Casimir-Delavigne
75006 Paris, France

Blackwell Wissenschaft, Meinekestrasse 4
D-1000 Berlin 15, Germany

Blackwell MZV, Feldgasse 13, A-1238 Wien
Austria

First published 1991

Printed in Great Britain at the
University Press, Cambridge

DISTRIBUTORS

  Marston Book Services Ltd
  PO Box 87
  Oxford OX2 0DT
  (*Orders*: Tel: 0865 791155
        Fax: 0865 791927
        Telex: 837515)

USA
  Blackwell Scientific Publications, Inc.
  3 Cambridge Center, Cambridge, MA 02142
  (*Orders*: Tel: (800) 759–6102)

Canada
  Oxford University Press
  70 Wynford Drive, Don Mills
  Ontario M3C 1J9
  (*Orders*: Tel: (416) 441–2941)

Australia
  Blackwell Scientific Publications
  (Australia) Pty Ltd, 54 University Street
  Carlton, Victoria 3053
  (*Orders*· Tel: (03) 347–0300)

British Library
Cataloguing in Publication Data

International Symposium on Drugs in
Competitive Athletics
  (1st; 1988, Brioni Islands, Yugoslavia)
  Drugs in competitive athletics:
  proceedings of the first International
  Symposium held on the islands of
  Brioni, Yugoslavia 29 May–2 June 1988.
  1. Sports. Drug abuse
  I. Title II. Shipe, James R.
  III. Savory, John IV. International
  Union of Pure and Applied Chemistry.
  Commission on Toxicology
  362.293088796

  ISBN 0–632–03181–6

Library of Congress
Cataloging in Publication Data

Drugs in competitive athletics: proceedings
  of the First International Symposium
  held on the islands of Brioni, Yugoslavia
  29 May–2 June 1988 / International
  Union of Pure and Applied Chemistry;
  edited by James R. Shipe, Jr. and John
  Savory.
     p. cm.
  "First International Symposium on
  Drugs in Competitive Athletics was held
  on the Islands of Brioni, Yugoslavia,
  from May 29 to June 2nd 1988 . . .
  organized under the auspices of IUPAC
  and the International Federation of
  Clinical Chemistry"—Pref.
    ISBN 0–632–03181–6
    1. Doping in sports—Congresses.
    2. Drug testing—Congresses.
  I. Shipe, James Roland. II. Savory,
  John, 1936– . III. International Union
  of Pure and Applied Chemistry.
  IV. International Federation of Clinical
  Chemistry. V. International
  Symposium on Drugs in Competitive
  Athletics (1st : 1988 : Brijuni, Croatia)
    [DNLM: 1. Doping in Sports—
  congresses. 2. Exertion—drug
  effects—congresses. 3. Substance
  Abuse—diagnosis—congresses.
  QT 260 D79445 1988]
  RC1230.D785 1991
  362.29' 088796—dc20

Contents

Section 2: Health Effects

Preface

The increasing awareness of the use of performance-enhancing drugs in competitive athletics prompted the International Union of Pure and Applied Chemistry (IUPAC) Commission on Toxicology to arrange an international conference devoted to analytical and clinical aspects of this problem. Although a few laboratories around the world, under the International Olympic Committee accreditation, had considerable expertise in testing for doping agents, the testing procedures were not widely available to the scientific community.

Thus, the First International Symposium on Drugs in Competitive Athletics was held on the Islands of Brioni, Yugoslavia, from 29 May to 2 June 1988. This symposium, organized under the auspices of IUPAC and the International Federation of Clinical Chemistry, was attended by participants from 19 countries, and included plenary lectures and contributed papers by many of the world's authorities on this subject.

There were open forum discussions on drug testing at major athletic events, with the panel members including the principal organizers of the drug testing for the Olympic Games held in Montreal (1976), Sarajevo (1984), Los Angeles (1984) and Universiade '87 Zagreb. The synopses of the open forum discussions and the scientific papers that were presented at the Symposium are published in this volume.

The organization of the Brioni Conference required the efforts of many scientists. The co-chairmen were Professors John Savory and Mirna Mikac-Dević, with the untiring assistance of M. Silvio Werson of Generalturist in Zagreb who arranged travel, conference facilities and social activities. The conference was a great success due in part to the idyllic location of the Brioni Islands. The authors gratefully acknowledge the generous support from sponsoring organizations and industry, and the assistance of Dr Allen Stevens of Blackwell Scientific Publications Ltd in expediting the publication of these proceedings.

JAMES R. SHIPE, JR
JOHN SAVORY

Section 1
Analytical Testing

Methodological imperatives and analytical requirements for the detection and identification of drugs misused in sport

Robert Dugal and Robert Massé

Institut National de la Recherche Scientifique (INRS-Santé), Université du Québec, 245 Hymus Blvd., Pointe-Claire (Montréal), Québec, H9R 1G6, Canada

Abstract -

The principles underlying the analysis of urine specimens for the purposes of detecting and identifying drugs misused by athletes and prohibited by international and national sport governing bodies are substantially different from other analytical toxicology undertakings such as emergency toxicology and the analysis of drugs in the workplace. Analytical strategies must take into account the type of sample which is available, the classes of drugs which must be screened for, the techniques that must be used, particularly for screening purposes, and the necessity for legal defensibility of results. Accordingly, the major methodological imperatives for the establishment of a comprehensive detection and identification analytical system are described and include considerations on extraction procedures, screening techniques, detection devices, computerized data acquisition, urinary excretion studies and confirmation procedures for the rigourous identification of detected compounds.

INTRODUCTION AND BACKGROUND

The testing of urine specimens for the purpose of diagnosing drug misuse or abuse is presently performed in a number of different situations, using a variety of analytical methods. Large volume screening of urine specimens dates back from the late sixties when methadone maintenance treatment programs for heroin addicts were established. Since the mid-70's, the most frequent applications of urine drug testing in man include pre-employment screening, monitoring of employees (specially operators of mass transit vehicles or of potentially dangerous equipment), routine screening of military personnel in some countries, of persons in probation programs, of individuals enrolled in drug abuse rehabilitation programs and of athletes - either during training (out-of-competition testing) or at actual competitive events. Generally, this latter activity is generally internationally known as doping control.

The problems of drug misuse in sport and the various measures that have been implemented to control it have many similarities to - and many differences with - the general problem of drug abuse in society. While the amount and kinds of drugs used by athletes can be qualified as impressive, one important difference between athletic and non-athletic drug misuse lies in the type of activity itself. In other words, an athlete takes - or will be given - many drugs that he would not take nor would be given if he were not an athlete. In the case of potentially performance-enhancing drugs, the substances are not taken for the purpose of restoring, improving or maintaining health, or for recreational purposes, but simply because an athlete or those around him believe that he will perform better with than without certain drugs. Another aspect of the misuse of drug in athletics that makes a clear definition of doping a very difficult task is the fact that in some cases the notion of justified use or blatant misuse depends on the circumstances of administration (ref. 1). If, for example, an injured gymnast is given an infiltration of a local anesthetic for the purpose of enabling him to rest better, the medical act involved is justified. However, if the same administration is made simply to numb the pain in order to allow the athlete to immediately return to competition (possibly resulting in further injury) this could conceivably be perceived as doping.

With these and other considerations in mind, international sport governing bodies - particularly the International Olympic Committee (IOC) - have, in the late 60's, established (and later periodically updated) lists of banned classes of drugs (doping classes and practices) according to the following policy elements: 1) to prevent and control the use of drugs which constitute dangers for an athlete or those around him; 2) to prevent drug misuse with the minimum interference with normal, correct and justified therapeutic use; 3) to ban only those drugs for which suitable analytical procedures could be devised to detect and unequivocally identify the compounds in urine and 4) to ban classes of drugs upon the pharmacological actions of members of the class but not attempt to produce a complete list of banned drugs, (ref. 2), which on an international basis is probably an impossible task. It should be mentioned, however, that the IOC banned blood doping in 1986 as well as human growth hormone and other peptides later, in spite of the fact that their exogeneous administration is thus far not detectable with the required certainty. This departure from policy element #3 above became necessary when documented evidence of this type of misuse became available.

The initial list of the IOC was established in 1967 and included only psychomotor stimulants and narcotic analgesics. Anabolic steroids were banned in 1975, β-adrenergic blocking agents in 1985 and diuretics in 1986. Thus, the concept of doping evolved from the strict notion of performance enhancement to eventually include pharmacological manipulations (such as the use of diuretics to dilute urine specimens and the use of Probenecid to decrease the urinary excretion of conjugated anabolic steroids). The current list of IOC banned classes of drugs and practices is reproduced in Table 1. Perusal of the list, combined to the considerations above, implicitly highlights the reasons for which analytical doping control differs substantially from, for instance, therapeutic drug monitoring, emergency and forensic toxicology as well as analysis of drugs in the workplace.

TABLE 1. List of doping classes and methods banned by the International Olympic Committee

I. DOPING CLASSES (with examples)

A. Stimulants
amfepramone – amfetaminil – amiphenazole – amphetamine – benzphetamine – caffeine – cathine chlorphentermine – clobenzorex – clorprenaline – cocaine – cropropamide – crothetamide – dimetamfetamine – ephedrine – etafedrine – ethamivan – etilamfetamine – fencamfamin – fenetylline – fenproporex – furfenorex – mefenorex – methamphetamine – methoxyphenamine – methylephedrine – methylphenidate – morazone – nikethamide – pemoline – pentetrazol – phendimetrazine – phenmetrazine – phentermine – phenylpropanolamine – pipradol – prolintane propylhexedrine – pyrovalerone – strychnine, **and related compounds**

B. Narcotic analgesics
alphaprodine – anileridine – buprenorphine – codeine – dextromoramide – dextropropoxyphen – diamorphine – dihydrocodeine – dipipanone – ethoheptazine – ethylmorphine – levorphanol – methadone – morphine – nalbuphine – pentazocine – pethidine – phenazocine – trimeperidine, **and related compounds**

C. Anabolic steroids
bolasterone – boldenone – clostebol – dehydrochlormethyltestosterone – fluoxymesterone – mesterolone – methandienone – methenolone – methyltestosterone – nandrolone – norethandrolone – oxandrolone – oxymesterone – oxymetholone – stanozolol – testosterone, **and related compounds**

D. β-adrenergic blocking agents
acebutolol – alprenolol – atenolol – labetalol – metoprolol – nadolol – oxprenolol – propranolol – sotalol, **and related compounds**

E. Diuretics
acetazolamide – amiloride – bendroflumethiazide – benzthiazide – bumetanide – canrenone – chlormerodrin – chlorthalidone – diclofenamide – ethacrynic acid – furosemide – hydrochlorothiazide – mersalyl – spironolactone – triamterene, **and related compounds**

F. Peptide hormones and analogues
Chorionic gonadotrophin – Corticotrophin – Growth hormone

II. METHODS

A. Blood doping B. Pharmacological, chemical and physical manipulations

III. CLASSES OF DRUGS SUBJECT TO CERTAIN RESTRICTIONS

A. Alcohol B. Marijuana C. Local anaesthetics D. Corticosteroids

---

Positivity for testosterone is based on a testosterone/epitestosterone ratio in excess of 6. Positivity for caffeine is based on a urinary concentration in excess of 12 mcg/ml.

DIFFERENCES BETWEEN ANALYTICAL DOPING CONTROL AND OTHER TYPES OF DRUG TESTING

1. The sample

For more than twenty years, doping control has been conducted with urine samples (and urine samples only) for a number of reasons which include the relative ease of non-invasively obtaining a readily accessible biological specimen, the usually much larger concentration of drug and/or metabolites in urine than in blood, the greater analytical possibilities of determining biotransformation products in a urine specimen and the fact that frozen urine specimens generally do not degrade significantly (unless thawed and refrozen frequently). There are, however, inherent disadvantages, the major one being that the interpretation of urinary concentrations is generally very difficult, due to such factors as inter-individual differences in urinary flow rate and in the ability to metabolize drugs.

Drawing blood samples would not however circumvent these difficulties. Internationally, there would be resistance or objections on religious grounds, not to mention the traumatic effect the procedure might have for most athletes after a competition. Moreover, with the currently accepted methodology in doping control, urine extraction gives rise to much less analytical interferences than blood. Finally, current methodology does not permit the detection of all banned substances using a blood sample of a reasonably limited volume, due in part to the large volume of distribution of several compounds. Thus, analytical procedures must be constructed taking in consideration the availability of one biological specimen only, which is, in addition, due to circumstances unique to sport drug testing, limited in volume and quite often diluted (low specific gravity).

2. Drugs screened for

Table 1 reveals that doping control laboratories must screen for **several classes of drugs** as well as pharmacologically and chemically **related compounds** in each class. Moreover, since these laboratories are very often involved in testing athletes participating in international events, they must have the ability to test not only for drugs manufactured in their home country but also for compounds marketed in other countries. For instance, Boldenone, Clostebol, Dehydrochlormethyltestosterone and Mesterolone listed under the class of Anabolic Steroids (Table 1) are not legally available in North America. Conversely, commercially available anabolic steroids such as Drostanolone, Mestanolone, Methandriol and others are not specifically mentioned on the list but should nevertheless be included in the analytical scheme. Likewise, the procedure should also include veterinary steroids which are (unfortunately) used by some athletes. The same considerations apply to all banned classes. These facts also make inadequate the use of techniques such as Enzyme Multiplied Immunoassay Technique (EMIT) and Radioimmunoassay (RIA) for screening listed psychomotor stimulants and narcotic analgesics since these methods were developed for compounds generally available in North America only.

Finally, the drugs for which a doping control laboratory must screen for are for the most part unique to sport. No laboratories other than doping control laboratories must routinely screen for β-adrenergic blocking agents, diuretics and anabolic steroids. This may be one of the most important factors in determining suitable analytical strategies.

3. Analytical techniques

There exists at present a wide variety of screening techniques used to detect the presence of drugs in urine specimens. Some are considered questionably to poorly specific (Radioimmunoassays, radioreceptor assays, enzyme multiplied immunoassays), others adequately specific (gas, liquid and thin-layer chromatography) and one, very highly specific (gas chromatography/mass spectrometry) (GC/MS). All these methods have advantages, disadvantages and limitations. Some are more expensive than others in terms of supplies but may require less manpower. Others are extremely rapid but less specific and, as a consequence, require a higher confirmation rate by more costly techniques. Some are very specific, but this may be a disadvantage of no little importance if one wishes the detection process to be comprehensive. Finally, such assays as EMIT for psychomotor stimulants or available RIA's (ref. 3,4) for anabolic steroids will give a class positive response which is not very informative and a significant number of samples may give rise to a positive screening test which will be eventually confirmed as a false positive (i.e. a real negative) by more specific physical-chemical techniques such as gas chromatography and GC/MS.

It is apparent from the above considerations that analytical strategies in doping control must be based on highly performing technology which meets a number of organizational and logistical imperatives. A consensus currently exists to the effect that the preliminary detection of drugs banned in sport must be conducted mainly by gas chromatography, high pressure liquid chromatography and gas chromatography/mass spectrometry.

These techniques are however relatively difficult to apply routinely with constant efficiency and require a high degree of expertise in spite of what the manufacturers of the corresponding equipment would like the user to believe. The pre-analytical sample manipulations (which include various hydrolysis and derivatization techniques) necessitate experience, chemical know-how and care. We know of no other area of analytical toxicology where some substances (anabolic steroids, narcotic analgesics, phenolic metabolites of psychomotor stimulants and, in some cases, β-adrenergic blocking agents) are systematically subjected to a preliminary screening by gas chromatography/mass spectrometry, which in other types of testing is generally reserved for confirmatory procedures.

TABLE 2. Summary of analytical procedures based on pharmacological classes

DOPING AGENTS CLASSES	EX-TRACTION	HYDRO-LYSIS a	DERIVATI-ZATION	SCREENING	CONFIRMATION Deriv.	Method
Most psychomotor stimulants	I	NO	NO	HRGC/NPD	NO	HRGC/MS
Some psychomotor stimulants and/or metabolites and conjugated narcotics analgesics	II	YES	YES	HRGC/NPD	YES	HRGC/MS
Some psychomotor stimulants and/or metabolites and unconjugated narcotics analgesics	I	NO	NO	HRGC/NPD	NO	HRGC/MS
Some psychomotor stimulants conjugated acidic metabolites	II	YES	NO	HRGC/NPD	NO	HRGC/MS
Pemoline and others, and quantitation of caffeine	III	NO	NO	HPLC/DAD	YES	HRGC/MS
Cocaine	NO	NO	NO	EMIT(V)	YES	HRGC/MS
Some opioids	NO	NO	NO	EMIT(V)	YES	HRGC/MS
β-blocking agents	II,IV	YES	YES	HRGC/MS	YES	HRGC/MS
Anabolic steroids	IV	YES	YES	HRGC/MS	YES	HRGC/MS
Testosterone/epitestosterone ratio	IV	YES	YES	HRGC/MS	YES	HRGC/MS
Diuretics (alkaline)	VI	NO	NO	HPLC/DAD	NO	HRGC/MS
Diuretics (acidic)	VII	NO	NO	HPLC/DAD	NO	HRGC/MS

HRGC/NPD: high resolution gas chromatography with nitrogen-phosphorous detection. HPLC/DAD high pressure liquid chromatography with UV-diode array detection. HRGC/MS: high resolution gas chromatography/mass spectrometry. EMIT: enzyme multiplied immunoassay technique. a : enzymatic hydrolysis for anabolic steroids and testosterone/epitestosterone ratio determination; acidic hydrolysis for all other classes of compounds.

Such comprehensive techniques and procedures are costly, labor intensive and in many cases time-consuming. They have however extraordinary advantages. Capillary gas chromatography will, for instance, allow for the detection of many drugs in a single analysis, or alternatively allow to make a definite diagnostic as to the absence of compounds belonging to a particular class. In conjunction with mass spectrometry for the detection of anabolic steroid usage, a wealth of information (particularly the detection of several endogeneous steroids) which can simply not be obtained by immunological techniques will be generated (ref. 5,6,7). In addition, many drugs which are detectable in one chromatographic procedure will also be detectable by at least another. A clear chromatographic resolution, combined to reproducible retention time parameters, screening procedure cross-over (i.e. the detection of a compound in more than one procedure) and the use of specific element (or mass specific) detection devices will in most cases generate sufficient information for the preliminary tentative identification of compounds present in a particular sample. Finally, quite a number of drugs which are not banned will be detected in one or several procedures. For example, several local anesthetics, antihistamine drugs, non-steroidal anti-inflammatory drugs and cough suppressants are detectable in either procedures I or II or both (Table 2). Some antibiotic and antibacterial drugs will be detected in procedure IV. When these analytical results are reconciled with the declarations athletes make at the time of sampling concerning the drugs they have received in the previous three days, they can generate interesting epidemiological data as to patterns of use of non-banned drugs. They also permit a proper scientific interpretation of analytical findings when drugs such as ephedrine and phenylpropanolamine are detected. This type of compound is banned in order to prevent athletes from using large doses of sympathomimetic amines as a substitute to amphetamine or other powerful stimulants. However, it must be recognized that inadvertent use of a cough syrup containing ephedrine can hardly be considered as doping. The capacity of the system to detect drugs such as antihistamines and cough suppressants, combined to the possibility of corroborating the analytical data with the athlete's declaration at the time of specimen collection, permits to a certain extent a pharmacological interpretation which may lead to warnings rather than to punitive measures.

4. International credibility and legal defensibility of results

All doping control laboratories conduct testing not only for national competitions but also at events including international participation. Due to the political sensitivity and media visibility of drug testing in sports and given the severe sanctions which generally follow a positive case, it is clear that the competence and credibility of these laboratories must be recognized and controlled on a regular basis. Mechanisms must be devised in order to eliminate the possibility of a false positive (which could possibly ruin an athlete's career) and to minimize the possibility of false negative results (which would taint the credibility of the testing process).

Another telling argument can be invoked for the use of the best available technology in order to ensure the accuracy, reliability, precision and reproducibility of doping control analyses. In the mid-80's, a number of court challenges of athletic drug testing programs were filed in some countries. Some challenges have focused on local constitutional issues such as invasion of privacy and unreasonable search and seizure. A surprising phenomenon however has emerged more recently in that not only results have been challenged but analytical methods as well. We know of at least one example where the reliability of a definitive method such as gas chromatography/mass spectrometry has been questioned by a court of law. The implication is clear: to technology of the highest possible degree of sophistication must correspond an unimpeachable scientific competence of personnel involved in the analytical work.

METHODOLOGICAL IMPERATIVES AND ANALYTICAL REQUIREMENTS

The above considerations naturally lead us to a general description, with reference to literature and yet unpublished data from our laboratories, of the methodological imperatives and the analytical requirements for the detection and identification techniques for drugs misused in sport, which are updated from ref. 8.

1. The extraction procedure should be as simple as possible but efficient enough to use small sample volumes (between 2 and 10 ml). It should cover all compounds likely to be screened for in the procedure. It is not essential however that all compounds be quantitatively extracted if the detection limits are sufficiently low.

Doping agents (with the exception of the vast majority of anabolic steroids) are nitrogen-containing compounds and their polarity vary from weakly acidic to strongly basic. For instance, anabolic steroids represent a relatively homogeneous class of neutral compounds and their recovery by solvent and solid phase extraction would theoretically not be expected to vary significantly by variations of pH, although we have shown important pH effects on percent recovery of oxandrolone (ref. 9) and some metabolites of stanozolol (ref. 10). On the other hand, diuretics present particular challenges due to their wide variety in chemical structures, their wide variety of functional groups, their wide range of pKa values and their low volatility. Their comprehensive screening analysis thus requires two different extraction procedures, one under acidic and the other under basic conditions (ref. 11).

High performance liquid chromatography, which is more suited than gas chromatography for separating large and polar compounds is used in conjunction with specific ultraviolet (UV) detection for screening purposes. This methodology has several advantages over GC and GC/MS screening methods, mainly because it does not require extensive sample preparation nor derivatization steps prior to analysis, while providing overall recoveries of more than 80% for most diuretics and for their metabolites (ref. 11).

2. The technique should be broad in scope and have the capability to detect a large number of different compounds while retaining the pre-requisites of methods developed for single compounds.

Let us consider the comprehensive detection of anabolic steroids and their metabolites as an example of this principle. The complexity of the analytical problem with anabolic steroids is due amongst other factors to 1) the large number of endogeneously produced steroids and their metabolites excreted in urine, 2) the number of anabolic steroids on the world market (about 40 different chemical entities), 3) the extensive metabolism of most anabolic steroids, 4) the structural and physical – chemical similarities between anabolic steroids and their metabolites and endogeneous steroids and 5) the high degree of sensitivity needed for the detection under the particular conditions of analytical doping control used as a deterrence instrument in sport.

One approach that was explored in the 70's (ref. 4,5) was the development of radioimmunoassays by directing the specificity of the antisera at distinctive features of orally active anabolic steroids (e.g. the $17-\alpha$-methyl group of the D-ring of the basic steroid molecule) and to the orally active and injectable derivatives of Nandrolone (absence of the C_{19} methyl group). This approach avoided the necessity of developing an antiserum for each anabolic steroid, which would not in any case be very practical for obvious reasons.

There were several difficulties with this strategy. First the antiserum was raised against a single parent compound with the result that the relative (and desirable) cross-reactivity of anabolic steroids belonging to the same group varied widely (from 100 to 0%). In short, the potential for false positives and negatives was high. Second, a positive screening result is not very informative in the sense that it indicates the possible presence of one or several compounds amongst many possibilities, including abnormal amounts of endogeneous material (ref. 12). Other difficulties are summarized in ref. 13.

In 1975, we initially circumvented these difficulties by devising a selected-ion monitoring procedure in both electron impact (EI) and chemical ionization (CI) GC/MS, whereby several groups of two or three specific ions were recorded and changed during the analysis according to the retention times of the steroids of interest (ref. 14). Considerable progress has been achieved since then, notably the use of solid phase extraction **in lieu** of the conventional solvent extraction procedures and the spectacular increase in separation efficiency afforded by the use of capillary column chromatography (ref. 10), but the basic principles are the same as those outlined in ref. 14. Recent (ref. 6,15,16) and current (ref. 7) methodology for the detection of anabolic steroids is based on these newer techniques and have resulted simultaneously in the generation of extremely useful and detailed information (such as the quantitative estimation of several endogeneous steroids) which cannot be obtained by the use of immunological techniques.

3. The detection device should show high sensitivity to a large number of drugs (and metabolites) excreted in urine in small quantities and low sensitivity to co-extractable components of the biological matrix.

The first comprehensive analytical procedure for psychomotor stimulants likely to be used in sports was published by Beckett and co-workers in 1967 (ref. 17). The use of gas chromatography was already well established, at the time, as the best technique for separating mixtures of chemically and structurally similar compounds. The use of the flame-ionization detector (FID) made possible the detection of a vast number of compounds because of its good general response, adequate sensitivity, excellent linear range and relative ease of operational variables control.

The possibilities for improvement were however limited simply due to the chemical nature of the drugs to be extracted, the nature of urine as a complex biological medium and the extraction solvents themselves. It is possible, for example, to decrease naturally occurring co-extractable components of urine by making some (time-consuming) purification steps before analysis or by varying the polarity of the solvent (in the two cases at the possible expense of percent recovery efficiency of the drugs). Similarly, it is possible to increase extraction yield by adding sodium chloride or another salt to the biological specimen. The advent of resin or solid phase extraction has improved the situation particularly for the extraction of conjugated steroids but not significantly for other banned drugs. Thus, if some significant improvements have been made in the last twenty years at some levels, the answer to the problem of sensitive and selective detection of nitrogen-containing drugs lied mainly in the detecting device itself by essentially increasing its sensitivity towards the substances of interest and by decreasing its undesirable capacity to detect co-extractable components of the biological matrix.

The introduction of the nitrogen phosphorous detector (NPD) in the early 70's provided this double capacity and its efficiency for the comprehensive detection of many nitrogen-containing compounds such as psychomotor stimulants and narcotic analgesics (ref. 8,18) relegated other detectors to oblivion. As a matter of fact, the only significant improvement since then has been in the area of column technology.

The introduction of the NPD detector almost eliminated the need for the time-consuming purification steps necessary to transform a biological sample into an analytical sample, because of its virtual absence of sensitivity (albeit when properly tuned (see ref.8)) towards molecules not containing one or more atoms of nitrogen, a characteristic that all doping agents (except most anabolic steroids) share. Furthermore, the suppression of potentially interfering peaks is accompanied by a significant increase in sensitivity towards nitrogen-containing molecules. These two factors made possible the production of much cleaner and readily interpretable chromatograms (ref. 8,18). As we shall see later, they also paved the way to a better utilization of laboratory computers as data acquisition and interpretation instruments.

4. The use of high performance separation techniques, and detection at very low limits should permit the preliminary identification of unknown compounds.

Although there exists some immunoassays that are very specific for certain compounds (e.g. for example cocaine metabolite, THC metabolite and amphetamine) the use of gas chromatoraphy or high pressure liquid chromatography with suitable detection devices (see below) provides a wealth of information which would not otherwise be obtained. An example is provided by what we have termed above "procedure cross-over" for the detection of psychomotor stimulants, narcotic analgesics (ref. 8) and later of β-adrenergic blocking agents as well as their respective metabolites (ref. 19).

Procedure I (see Table 2) involves a single-step extraction at an highly alkaline pH and Procedure II involves an acid hydrolysis step (in order to liberate the base moiety of metabolic conjugates) followed by extraction at pH 9.2 and derivatization by trifluoroacetic anhydride (TFAA). The analytical samples are then submitted to gas chromatography with nitrogen selective detection. One of the major problem with the GC analysis of derivatized urinary extracts is that many extraneous peaks are usually present and can generally be only suppressed through a decrease in detector sensitivity. Extensive studies made in this laboratory in the seventies (ref. 8) and later confirm that the use of TFAA constitutes the best compromise between completeness of reaction for all compounds of interest and analysis requirements such as relatively clean and readily interpretable chromatograms.

One of the main advantages of this derivatizing technique is the fact that the discriminating power of the nitrogen-phosphorous detector can be maximized since the stability of the detector is, over time, less affected by contamination of the derivatized compounds than if one would use other types of derivatizing agents, particularly silicon-based derivatizing agents. Secondly, many compounds detected in Procedure I will appear as such or, more often, as their TFA derivatives in Procedure II, along with their conjugated metabolites not detected in Procedure I, thus providing preliminary evidence or indication that the sample is a potential positive when data from both procedures are reconciled.

The well known technological problems associated with the routine use of capillary columns were surmounted in the late 70's, to the extent that we were, for example, able to conduct all screening procedures with such columns at the 1980 Lake Placid Olympic Winter Games. Capillary columns provide a resolution efficiency which is of one to two orders of magnitude higher than conventional packed columns. Consequently, they are primarily used for resolution of complex mixtures such as those encountered in the urinary matrix. The use of the so-called "immobilized stationary phases" has greatly improved column inertness and sensitivity of screening and confirmation methods, which are clear advantages in GC of samples containing a subnanogram concentration of a prohibited drug. An effective utilization of capillary columns however requires appropriate instrumentation and periodical testing of the system and column performance is essential to maintain valid qualitative and quantitative data. In the specific case of compounds, whose chromatography is affected by acid-base properties of the column surface (i.e. amphetamine, stanozolol, etc.), it is necessary to regularly diagnose column status by testing with mixtures of selected "molecular probes". For detailed considerations on capillary column gas chromatography, see ref. 20.

5. The method should use the software capabilities of modern laboratory computers to compensate for problems arising from the physical-chemical constraints of system expansion.

Another significant technological development of the early seventies was the interfacing of computers to laboratory instruments. Before the advent of this technology, the interpretation and quantitation of results had to be made visually, retention times had to be calculated on the chromatogram with a ruler and quantitation had to be effected by geometric techniques which were often cumbersome. The computer not only eliminated these tasks but allowed some complex chromatographic functions and calculations to be realized automatically. Computer interfacing of gas chromatographs (and mass spectrometers) offers a number of advantages in the screening of drugs and their metabolites extracted from biological materials. One of the most interesting features of currently available software is the possibility of constructing computer methods allowing direct comparison, via the central processing unit, of the sample's characteristics to previously made calibrations stored in memory banks. When a sample shows a peak with a retention time identical (within a certain retention time window) to that of any substance included in the data bank, it automatically identifies and quantitates the peak, through the response factor, as that particular substance. Identity confirmation is accomplished afterwards by gas chromatography/mass spectrometry.

The computer interfacing of instruments through analog to digital converters is a powerful tool for data interpretation. The capability of process automation from sample introduction to final readout reduces the possibilities of human error and speeds up calculations since data systems record all raw chromatographic data, calculate retention times and peak areas, normalize them, correct for baseline drift, integrate unusually shaped peaks by special algorithms, compare available values for primary peak identification, quantitate peaks according to stored calibrations, and produce a finished analytical report. Automatic data acquisition is thus an essential feature of GC, HPLC and GC/MS for the analysis of drugs in biological fluids, especially in situations where a large number of complex samples have to be processed rapidly. In order for this to be possible, it is necessary to have element and/or mass selective detection devices to make the enormous capabilities of data handling systems an analytical asset.

An example of the power of this technique is provided by the method we have developed (ref. 7) for the preliminary screening of anabolic steroids and their metabolites by selected-ion monitoring gas chromatography/mass spectrometry. The most current version is reproduced in Table 3. Retention times of peaks of interest are initially determined, a number of significant ions (one to four) are chosen and the computer instructed as to dwell times. These data are based on the previous GC/MS analysis of samples obtained from authentic reference materials and urinary excretion studies in man.

In the analysis of an unknown sample (see ref. 7), data are first computer-analyzed to locate the external standard, calculate relative retention time (RRT) and integrate peaks of interest at preselected m/z and RRT values. This first step in data analysis provides information about the chromatographic and MS status of the GC/MS system used as well as on the level of the endogenous steroids of interest. The ion fragmentograms are then plotted in time-windows corresponding to those used for SIM screening, and searches for the potential presence of two, three or four peaks eluting in coincidence at proper RRT values are performed. The absence of coeluting peaks in a specific time-window is interpreted as the absence of the corresponding steroid in the urine specimen. On the other hand, the presence of coeluting peaks indicates the potential presence of a steroid, providing that their RRT values are in accordance with reference values obtained from human studies with the corresponding steroid. Ion peaks are then integrated and peak-ion ratios compared to those from reference compounds and urinary metabolites from human studies. Meanwhile, the sample is reinjected in both the SIM and repetitive scanning modes to assess identity by comparison of steroid profiles and to confirm data from preliminary screening. Next, two aliquots of the urine specimen are re-extracted, taking into account the features of the excretion profile of the steroid and the concentration of the metabolites in the specimen. The profile of the urinary metabolites is then obtained using SIM and repetitive scanning of short and extended mass ranges and compared to that obtained from human studies. For final and unambiguous assignment of identity, the data are finally assessed and validated by comparison with data from reference materials and urinary samples obained from volunteers known to have been administered a particular steroid.

6. Excretion patterns of each drug and/or of its metabolite(s) should be established (whenever ethically feasible) using the method which will eventually be used in the screening process.

The elaboration of an integrated, comprehensive system for the detection of drugs and their metabolites also relies heavily on the knowledge of the pharmacokinetic behavior of the parent compound. The necessity of acquiring fundamental information concerning the

TABLE 3. Partial list of acquisition parameters for the selected ion monitoring GC/MS screening of anabolic steroids and their metabolites

Steroid	rf (min.)	Monitored ions (dwell time)	Group
Androstan-17-one	17.8	331.3 (50)	1 (16.5)
Androsterone and Ethiocholanolone TMS-ethers	21.2, 21.4	272.2 (50)	1
Nandrolone metabolite 1	20.1	420.4 405.4 315.3 (100) (100) (50)	1
metabolite 2	20.9	420.4 405.4 315.3 (100) (100) (50)	1
metabolite 3	21.3	420.4 405.4 315.3 (100) (100) (50)	1
Boldenone metabolite 1	20.3	432.4 194.1 (100) (50)	1
Methenolone metabolite 1	22.9	446.4 431.4 (100) (50)	2 (22.0)
Dehydroepiandrosterone	23.0	432.4 (50)	2
Methyltestosterone and Mestanolone metabolite	23.3	450.4 435.4 143.1 (100) (50) (50)	2
Mesterolone metabolite 1	23.3	448.4 433.4 (100) (50)	2
metabolite 2	24.0	448.4 433.4 (100) (50)	3 (23.4)
parent	24.2	448.4 433.4 (100) (50)	2
Epitestosterone	23.5	432.4 (100)	3
Trenbolone epimetabolite	23.8	412.4 307.3 (100) (100)	3
Boldenone parent	24.2	430.4 206.2 (100) (50)	3
Testosterone	24.4	432.4 (100)	3
Drostanolone parent	24.6	448.4 433.4 141.1 (100) (50) (50)	3
Bolasterone metabolite 1	24.8	449.4 374.3 143.1 (100) (50) (50)	4 (24.7)
Chlortestosterone parent	25.0	466.4 451.4 431.4 (100) (100) (50)	4
Methenolone parent	25.1	446.4 431.4 195.1 (100) (50) (50)	4
17α-methyl-5α-androstane 3-β,17-β-diol	25.1	435.4 143.1 (50) (50)	4
Mibolerone parent	25.5	446.4 431.4 301.3 (100) (50) (50)	4

Steroid	rf (min.)	Monitored ions (dwell time)				Group
Fluoxymesterone						
metabolite 1	26.9	642.5 (100)	552.5 (50)	462.4 (50)	143.1 (50)	5 (25.7)
Norethandrolone						
metabolite 1	27.1	538.5 (100)	421.4 (50)	245.2 (50)		5
Zeranol	27.1	538.5				5
parent	27.4	538.5				
Formebolone						
metabolite	27.3	534.5 (100)	444.4 (50)	389.3 (50)	143.1 (50)	5
Oxandrolone						
parent	28.0	378.3	363.3	143.1		6 (27.5)
Methandienone						
metabolite 1	28.2	532.5 (100)	517.5 (50)			6
Fluoxymesterone						
parent	29.1	552.5 (100)	462.4 (50)	407.4 (50)		6
Oxymetholone						
metabolite 1	29.4	550.5 (50)	460.4 (50)	143.1 (50)		7 (29.3)
metabolite 2	29.9	640.5 (100)	550.5 (50)	460.4 (50)	143.1 (50)	7
Oxymesterone						
metabolite 1	29.8	538.5 (100)	523.5 (50)	143.1 (50)		7
parent	30.1	534.5 (100)	143.1 (50)			7
Furazabol						
parent	30.1	402.4 (100)	387.3 (50)	143.1 (50)		7
Dehydrochlormethyl-testosterone						
metabolite 1	29.9	170.1 (50)	143.1 (50)			7
metabolite 2	33.1	315.3 (50)	243.2 (50)	170.1 (50)	143.1 (50)	
Stanozolol						
parent	32.9	472.4 (100)	457.4 (100)	143.1 (50)		8
Furazabol						
metabolite 1	35.1	490.4 (100)	231.2 (50)	218.2 (50)		9 (33.5)
Stanozolol						
metabolite 1	34.9	560.5 (100)	545.5 (100)	254.2 (100)	143.1 (50)	9
metabolite 2	35.1	560.5 (100)	545.5 (100)	254.2 (100)	143.1 (50)	9

Experimental conditions may be found in Massé et al., (ref.7). Two internal standards are used (Androstan-17-one and 17-α-methyl-5α-androstane-3β,17β-diol). The first number in parentheses in the right-hand column indicates the time at which data acquisition is initiated and the other numbers in the same column indicate the times at which the ion group is changed.

absorption, distribution, biotransformation, and elimination of drugs, as well as data concerning factors which may affect these processes, was well emphasized by Beckett and co-workers (ref. 17). The urinary metabolic products must be determined in order to construct an appropriate method. It makes little sense, for example, to screen for the parent compound if the substance is excreted mainly as metabolites. Furthermore, it is necessary to at least quantitatively estimate the excretion pattern of each drug in order to screen for the major metabolite(s), thus increasing the degree of retrospectivity in the analysis, which is essential for the detection of anabolic steroid misuse (since athletes are known to interrupt administration in anticipation of announced tests).

The excretion rate of a number of drugs is influenced by urinary pH and output, which both fluctuate throughout the day. For example, about 30-40% of a dose of amphetamine is excreted unchanged over 48 hours under normal fluctuating pH conditions. However, if the urine is rendered acidic for the same period this proportion increases to 60-70% and falls below 10% if the urine is rendered alkaline (ref. 21,22). This reality must be taken into account when elaborating analytical strategies.

Excretion studies are not only useful in many respects but necessary. First, they enable the validity testing (determination of detection limits, evaluation of background noise and matrix interferences, percent extraction recovery, and determination of proper chromato-graphic conditions) of the chosen procedure for all drugs under study. They also permit the acquisition of useful information concerning the metabolism of drugs of abuse. The quantitation of drugs at various times after administration allows the laboratory to accu-mulate data which can later be used to formulate a scientific judgment concerning the con-centration of a particular drug and/or metabolite in a sample, in situations where an esti-mation of the concentration is necessary. Furthermore, such excretion studies, if per-formed in a systematic manner (i.e. serial collection of urine specimens over a period of several days) permit the determination of detection periods after administration of a single dose (ref. 9) and approximate extrapolation of retrospectivity after multiple doses.

7. Confirmation of potential positive results should be made through the use of reliable and indisputable techniques. At present, only mass spectrometry linked to gas chromato-graphy (GC/MS) or high pressure liquid chromatography (HPLC/MS) meets the current scienti-fic imperatives.

The development and competent application of high-quality confirmation methods for drug analysis, specially designed to meet the stringent needs and requirements identified above represent the classical but evermore important responsibility of the scientist. In that context, the use of multi-stage instruments (GC/MS, LC/MS, etc.) incorporating extremely sensitive and specific detectors is essential to achieve this task. Confirmation procedures of potential positive results for anabolic steroids require a high level of specificity due to the presence in the sample of endogeneous steroids exhibiting similar structural features. There should be in the methodology used an appropriate balance between sample preparation and instrumental specificity, given the nature and amounts of the steroid of interest and interfering substances. In some cases, a lack of specificity can be compensated for when the steroid and contaminant (which could be an endogeneous urinary steroid) have different response patterns. Furthermore, overlapping responses such as in ion chromatograms or mass spectra can be mathematically resolved given sufficient measurement precision and response pattern differences.

In order to maximize accuracy, precision and sensitivity of the confirmation analysis, ins-trumental and sample blanks are previously analyzed in order to characterize the nature and origin of any contamination or interference and to measure instrumental baseline and background responses. These tests provide valuable information about sample preparation efficiency, actual status of the GC/MS system and detection limits for the analysis of minute amounts. In the best of circumstances, the mean value of the blank might be expected to be constant and its fluctuations ("noise") normally distributed.

The confirmation methods are tailor-designed to suit the specific physical-chemical and chromatographic properties of a given drug and/or its metabolites and take into account its characteristic urinary excretion profile. Thus, confirmation methods, given the steroid previously detected, differ, in some cases, substantially from the screening methods by the application of specific sample preparation steps and/or new parameters for instrumental analysis. Metabolic fingerprints of anabolic steroid metabolites (ref. 7) have been shown to be very valuable for the qualitative identification of the parent steroid, in cases where it is extensively metabolized and barely detectable in urine. Although adequate sample preparation methodologies and state-of-the art instrumental analysis are essential prerequisites to high quality of analytical results, the best chance for undisputable and quality results lies with the skill and knowledge of the scientific personnel in designing efficient analytical strategies for sample preparation and analysis, rather than simply utilizing a readily available multi-element method in the hope that its performance characteristics will provide a unique solution.

8. Quality control procedures should include the mandatory use of an internal standard in all procedures.

Notwithstanding cost and complexity factors, the advantages of combining the use of powerful chromatographic separation techniques with the use of highly selective and detection devices are obvious from the considerations above. However, the need for stringent quality control procedures is an inevitable consequence of the multiplicity of the analytical methods used in doping control.

Doping control analyses are generally performed by batch. Thus, batch processing of a set of samples each containing an internal standard, along with different blanks (water, reagent and solvent) and reference material (calibration mixtures of authentic reference standards and reference urines) generates quality control information which is of immediate diagnostic value for procedural or instrumental deficiencies and which can be used to introduce corrective mesures. Moreover, if these batch data are generated and presented in a continuous manner, they can be reviewed by external referees in case of challenges (ref. 23).

Each batch of specimens to be screened should include one control urine specimen known not to contain any drug (urine blank), one or more specimens fortified with known standards, which may be spiked or which may represent a mixture of excretion studies performed under controlled conditions. In addition, internal proficiency test specimens should be tested periodically.

Similar controls should be analyzed in parallel with confirmation tests, using positive controls with the drug or metabolite in the same concentration range in order to correct for concentration-depending deviations of retention times and mass spectral fragmentation patterns. Procedures to ensure that carry-over does not contaminate the testing of a particular specimen should be implemented (e.g. tests for interferences, blank urine, reagent blank, water blank, solvent blank). The use of an internal standard in all chromatographic procedures is mandatory: the addition of an internal standard compensates not only for extraction losses but allows for the control of retention times reproducibility and detector response.

CONCLUSION

We have reviewed some methodological imperatives and analytical requirements particular to drug testing in sports. The scientific and technical information accumulated over the last twenty years has been synthesized and presented using what we thought were the most significant components of a comprehensive analytical scheme. It can be said that classical methods of doping using conventional drugs can now be routinely and efficiently detected, provided that correct procedures are implemented for the selection and sampling of athletes.

However, new challenges are already emerging. In an attempt to circumvent current detection procedures, athletes are reported to increasingly resort to the administration of physiological substances such as human growth hormone, human chorionic gonadotropin, autologous blood transfusions and, more recently, erythropoietin as substitutes to conventional drugs for the purposes of performance enhancement. Definitive methods for the detection and/or identification of these practices are currently lacking. It is probable that research priorities in doping control will shift from the techniques of organic and analytical chemistry to those physiological chemistry, endocrinology, hematology and molecular biology. The complexity of the work is thus likely to increase significantly in the 90's and will require the structuring of multidisciplinary interventions to solve these new problems.

REFERENCES

1. R. Dugal and M. Bertrand, in Proceedings of a feature presentation on spectroscopy and drug abuse, Ed. by G.A. Neville, Spectroscopy Society of Canada, 1975, pp. 82-116.

2. A.H. Beckett, in Proceedings of the International Athletic Foundation World Symposium on doping in sport, Ed. by P. Bellotti, G. Bengi and A. Ljungqvist, FIDAL Centro Studi & Ricerche, Rome, 1988, pp. 1-11.

3. R.V. Brooks, R.G. Firth and N.A. Summer, Brit. J. Sports Med, 9, 89-95 (1975).

4. R.V. Brooks, G. Jeremiah, W.A. Webb et al., J. Steroid Biochem, 11, 913-917 (1979).

5. M. Donike, J. Zimmerman, V.R. Barwald et al., Deutsche Z. Sportmed. 35, 14-24 (1984).

6. D.H. Catlin, R.C.Kammerer, C.K. Hatton et al., Clin. Chem. 33, 319-327 (1987).

7. R. Massé, C. Ayotte and R. Dugal, J. Chromatog. (Biomed. Applic), 489 23-50 (1989).

8. R. Dugal, R. Massé, G. Sanchez et al., J. Anal. Toxicol., 4, 1-12 (1980).

9. R. Massé, H. Bi, C. Ayotte, and R. Dugal, Biomed. Environ. Mass Spectrom. 18, 429-438 (1989).

10. R. Massé, C. Ayotte, H. Bi and R. Dugal, J. Chromatog. (Biomed. Applic), 497, 17-37 (1989).

11. S. Cooper, R. Massé and R. Dugal, J. Chromatog. (Biomed. Applic.), 489, 65-88 (1989).

12. R. Dugal, C. Dupuis and M.J. Bertrand, Brit. J. Sports Med., 11, 162-169 (1977).

13. C.K. Hatton and D.H. Catlin, Clin. Lab., Med., 7, 655-668 (1987).

14. M. Bertrand, R. Massé and R. Dugal, Farm. Tijds. Belg., 55, 85-101 (1978).

15. G.P. Cartoni, M. Ciardi, A. Giarrusso et al., J. Chromatog., 279, 515-522 (1983).

16. R. Massé, C. Ayotte and R. Dugal, in Developments in analytical methods in pharmaceutical, biomedical and forensic sciences, Ed. by G. Piemonte, F. Tagliaro, M. Marizo and A. Frigerio, Plenum, New York, 1987, pp. 183-190.

17. A.H. Beckett, G.T. Tucker and A.C. Moffat, J. Pharm. Pharmacol., 19, 273-294 (1967).

18. M. Donike, L. Jaenicke, Stratmann and W. Hollmann, J. Chromatog., 52, 237-250 (1970).

19. S. Cooper, R. Massé and R. Dugal, unpublished results.

20. C.A. Cramers and P.A. Leclercq, CRC Critical Reviews in Analytical Chemistry, 20, 117-147 (1988).

21. A.H. Beckett and M. Rowland, Nature, 204, 1203-1204 (1964).

22. H.A. Beckett and M. Rowland, J. Pharm. Pharmacolol., 17, 628-639 (1965).

23. R. Dugal and M. Donike, in Proceedings of the International Symposium on dug abuse in sport, ed. by Jongsei Park, Seoul, in press (1989).

Endocrine effects and immunoassay procedures of anabolics

Richard Hampl and Luboš Stárka

Research Institute of Endocrinology, 116 94 Praha 1,
Czechoslovakia

Abstract - The main side effects of exogenous anabolics and
androgens on endocrine system of healthy humans, especially
active sportsmen are reviewed. It includes their action on
growing and developing organism and the impact of their intake
on reproductive system. The role of anabolics as potential
risk factor in development of atherosclerosis is also
mentioned. The possible sites of action of anabolics and
androgens in the light of recent advances of molecular
endocrinology are discussed. The contribution of immunoassays
as an analytical tool to the detection of the abuse of these
steroids as well as to following their fate in organism is
outlined in the second part of the review. The methodological
achievments concerning determination of the main classes of
anabolics and androgens including testosterone preparations
are surveyed.

INTRODUCTION

Attempts to use anabolic - androgenic steroids in humans started as
early as in late thirties when their effect on nitrogen retention was first
described by Kenyon et al. (ref. 1). The first reported use of these drugs
in non-clinical setting was during World War II, when both fighting sides
took them to enhance the aggressiveness of troops. The use of anabolics in
sports is usually atributed to the late John B.Ziegler, team physician of
American weight lifters, who described in 1954 the improvement of performance
following steroid intake. As demonstrated at Olympic Games in Tokyo ten years
later, the abuse of anabolic steroid in power athletics and other sports
became widespread and it has been persisting till the present time.

The accumulating knowledge in steroid endocrinology in sixties and seventies,
the discovery of sophisticated feedback relationships of mutual hormonal
control and the findings of receptor-mediated mechanism of steroid hormone
action in target tissues arose logically the question of the impact of exogenous steroid intake on these sensitive but vulnerable mechanisms. The
serious warning soon appeared from the physicians, concerning the expected
as well as unexpected side effects of exogenous steroids. These misgivings
as well as ethical considerations led to a ban of these drugs by a majority
of official authorities dealing with health risks in sports. This consequently initiated the search for a convenient analytical tools for detection of a
drug abuse, taking into account particular requirements of specimen
aquisition, discussed also in this volume.

The diversity of actions of anabolic steroids in human organism is very
large. In the following we have attempted to review some of the most important
effects of these drugs on endocrine system, to point to some connections and
open questions, especially concerning the effect of anabolics on reproduction
and the growing organism. Some aspects are discussed in the light of recent
findings on molecular endocrinology of steroid hormone action. In the second
part we have tried to survey the contribution of immunoassay techniques to
up-to-date state of art of doping control.

ENDOCRINE EFFECTS OF ANABOLIC STEROIDS

Effect of anabolics on female reproduction

In women the well known signs of virilization are due to the androgenic effects of anabolics, manifesting mainly on secondary sex organs. Deepening of voice, hirsutism or hypertrichosis accompanied eventually by androgenic alopecia were observed, as well as an appearance of male pattern of body building (ref. 2). Both hypersexuality and frigidity were recorded in women taking anabolics. These changes are often irreversible. We have had an opportunity to follow up the group of female-to-male transsexual women, wishing the gender change and treated with various androgens or anabolics (testosterone undecanoate, testosterone isobutyrate, methyltestosterone). Besides expected hormonal changes due to the effect on hypothalamo-pituitary-gonadal axis, all developed typical masculine anthropometric features during three months treatment and these changes were maintained at least one year after cessation of steroid administration (ref. 3). Testosterone and its 17β-esters, bolasterone, drostanolone, fluoxymesterone, methyltestosterone and nandrolone (for full chemical names of anabolics and androgens mentioned here and further in the text see Table 1) are believed to be the most androgenic as concerns the virilization effects in women (ref. 4). However, there is a wide interindividual variation with respect not only to the drug, but also to dosis producing side effects.

The chemical nature of some anabolics and their ability to occupy the receptor binding sites of natural hormones in target tissues render them both anti-estrogenic and gestagenic. Antiestrogenic are mainly C-18 steroids as nandrolone and its 17α-alkylderivatives (methylnandrolone, norethandrolone). The side chain at 17α-position and/or the planarity of A-ring confer to some of them also gestagenic properties (e.g.ethylestrenol, methylnandrolone, norethandrolone or nandrolone) (ref. 5). Their action at central level leads to suppression of gonadotrophins, resulting accordingly in disturbances of endogenous steroid production and to disorders of menstrual cycle. Andro-stanolone, clostebol, ethylestrenol, thiomesterone, nandrolone and norethan-drolone were shown to be the most potent antigonadotrophic agents, the two latter possessing also the highest anticyclic activity (ref. 2). Similar effects were reported in women undergoing an intensive exercise (ref. 6,7). The effect of steroid intake is then additive to the latter, leading often to severe endocrine impairments in women competitors using anabolics.

Effect of anabolics on male reproduction

The effect of anabolic steroids on male reproduction attracted attention since early sixties when often controversial experience was made as the influence on male reproductive functions concerns. The more recent reports (ref. 8,9,10,11) demonstrated unequivocally the negative impact of anabolics administration on spermatogenesis. There was recorded a drastic decrease of sperm count after nortestosterone esters (ref. 8,11) so that it was concluded that these steroids, together with analogues of gonadoliberins are suitable for eliciting temporary infertility. The representative studies of Finnish authors (ref. 9,10) were carried out in power athletes who used many different preparations at the same time (including testosterone and nandrolone esters, methandienone and stanazolol) and underwent an intensive training. The observed changes were compared with a placebo group on the same training regime. The anabolics caused a significant decrease of sperm count (with a retained volume of an ejaculate) or even azoospermia (6 out 7). In those men without azoospermia the percentage of spermatozoa with normal configuration decreased significantly, too.

The administration of anabolics led also to a considerable decline of both gonadotrophins (ref. 10,11) during several weeks. When nandrolone ester (hexoxyphenyl propionate) was given, only very low testosterone levels, occurring in castrates could be measured (ref. 11). In the group obtaining also testosterone preparates, testosterone levels were increased but immediately after finishing of the treatment they decreased markedly. The temporary enhancement of testosterone was followed by that of estradiol, which rose 7-fold to values, typical for females (ref. 10). The authors (ref. 10) measured also cortisol and ACTH and they have found a significant decrease of the latter, possibly due to a corticoid-like effect of some of anabolics, taken in high doses. Anyway, there is not much known about the effect(s) of

anabolics on the pituitary - adrenal axis. We are convinced that this might
be of interest in the light of possible compensation mechanisms developed in
agonadal subjects or in human with impaired gonadal function (ref. 12,13).

In the past decade, much attention has been paid to antiestrogen treatment
of oligozoospermic men. It provided a suitable model for evaluation of inter-
relationships between hypothalamo - pituitary - gonadal production and the
ways how to influence it by exogenous factors, e.g. drugs (ref. 14,15).
Some methodological approaches and findings from this area may be worthwhile
for deeper insight into the endocrine background of the changes caused by
administration of anabolics to healthy men. Recently, in addition to the
long-term regulatory systems comprised of FSH / inhibin and LH / testosterone
there have been identified short-loop systems within the testis, ensuring by
means of pro-opiomelanocortin derived peptides the communication between
various cell components in the testis (ref. 16). The question arises, how
anabolics do influence these mechanisms, responsible for functioning of the
testis as a true biological clock.

Anabolic steroids and the risk of ischemic heart disease
The relationship between physical fitness and a lipid spectrum in serum,
preferring high density lipoprotein (HDL) cholesterol to the low density
lipoprotein bound cholesterol is well known. On the other hand there were
controversial reports dealing with lipoprotein composition in power athletes.
It has been also reported that administration of exogenous testosterone as
well as of anabolics reduced plasma HDL-cholesterol. For the literature see
Alén and Rahkila (ref. 17). In this study the authors showed that not an
intensive training, but exclusively an intake of anabolic steroids (a mixture
of testosterone and nandrolone esters in combination with perorally active
steroids as methandienone and/or stanazolol) is responsible for observed
considerable decrease of HDL cholesterol. They concluded that anabolics are
a risk factor for development of atherosclerosis. These results were confirmed recently by Dutch investigators (ref. 18) in a larger group of 45 body
builders, whose competitive level was lower than that of top performance
athletes. A significant decrease of HDL-cholesterol, parallelled by a
significant rise of LDL-cholesterol and corresponding changes in other lipoprotein fractions were found in users of anabolics as compared with controls.

It would be of interest to confront these results with large scale studies
attempting to elucidate the role of sexual hormones as a hypothetical risk
factor in development of atherosclerosis or ischemic heart disease (for
review see ref. 19). It was demonstrated repeatedly that men who underwent
or suffered from ischemic heart disease had elevated levels of estradiol
accompanied with decreased testosterone. Moreover, these alterations correlated well with impaired glucose tolerance in these subjects (ref. 20). So
far it is not clear whether the altered hormonal levels are true risk factor
or whether this shift in balance between the sexual hormones does represent
a compensation mechanism.

Endocrine effect of androgenic / anabolic steroids on growing organism
The danger of anabolic - androgenic steroids misuse in adolescency refers
also to their effect on growth. Soon after introduction of these drugs into
the therapy experience was made that these steroids are able to promote a
skeletal growth, possibly due to their anabolic effect on bone matrix
formation and consequently on a development of musculature. At the same time,
however, androgens and anabolics can accelerate a skeletal maturation by an
early closure of the epiphyses, resulting in a premature arrest of linear
growth. Both these effects depend on the type of the drug, duration of
treatment, the dose and dosage regime and, of course, there are considerable
interindividual variations. The recommended dosage of various preparations
are based mainly on clinical experience and empiricism. The digest of the
literature of this topics can be found in the monography of Kochakian (ref.
21) or in the more recent papers mentioned in the further text.

It should be stressed here that an optimal skeleton growth depends on inter-
play of both androgens (or anabolics) and growth hormone (GH), which act
synergistically and they are influenced by each other. The more recent studies
on endocrine effects of various exogenous hormones and drugs on feedback
mechanisms of endocrine control emphasize the importance of modulation of
the pulsatile release of pituitary factors including GH. There are several
studies concerning the effect of steroid exposure on GH release, mainly in

hypogonadal men (see e.g. ref. 22) or in prepubertal boys with delayed growth (ref. 23,24). These reports document well the diversity of the effects of steroid exposure on GH release pattern. There was found e.g. a considerably higher response of GH secretion to testosterone over axandrolone in children with delayed growth. Testosterone propionate induced an enhancement of both total GH secretion and its mean pulse amplitude, but not the frequency of the pulses (ref. 22). In this connection we would like to remind here the existing differences between the sites of negative feedback action of andro- gens and estrogens, resulting in different release of both gonadotrophins. Testosterone and its analogues act at the hypothalamic level by decreasing the frequency of pulses of LH release, whereas estrogens act in both the hypothalamus and pituitary and influence mainly the amplitude of FSH pulses (ref. 14,15). One may expect interesting similarities as concerns the different modulation of the secretion of GH and other growth factors (somato- statin, somatomedines) by various anabolics.

The receptor mediated mechanism of action of anabolics
Since seventies it has been postulated that steroids do exert their action in target tissues through their receptors. Receptor proteins of each of the main classes of steroid hormones (i.e. androgens, estrogens, progestins and both gluco- and mineralocorticoids) have been described and characterized in cytosol (as a supernatant of a high-speed ultracentrifugation of a tissue homogenate) in a number of tissues. For years so called two-step mechanism was accepted, according to which unoccupied receptors are localized in the cytoplasm and following steroid binding the hormone-receptor complex migrates into the nucleus, where it interacts with chromatin to bring about changes in target cell function. Recently, at least as estrogenic receptors concern, this model has been questioned. Monoclonal antibodies against purified receptors have been prepared and used in immunohistochemical experiments, in which they have been found predominantly in a nuclear fraction. It was concluded that the receptors may not be localized at given time in a single subcellular compartment, but rather exist in a dynamic equilibrium between the cytoplasm and nucleus (ref. 25,26).

The knowledge of action of anabolics in various tissues, predominantly, how- ever, in muscle led logically to the question, whether also in this tissue does the receptor-mediated mechanism take part. The kinetics of amino acid and/or nucleotide incorporation and the chronology of consecutive events involved in protein synthesis de novo following administration of anabolics both in vivo and in vitro supported this suggestion (for a literature see e.g. ref. 27). Indeed, the receptor binding sites for androgens and anabolics, distinct from glucocorticoid receptor have been identified and characterized in various preparations of a muscle tissue (ref. 28,29,30). It was demonstra- ted that anabolics can exert their anticatabolic action also by occupation of glucocorticoid receptors but not vice versa (ref. 31,32).

Much attention has been paid to correlation of biological efficiency of various androgenic / anabolic steroids with their in vitro binding in prostate or seminal vesicles (reflecting the "androgenic" activity) and in muscle cytosol. We will not review here a vast number of papers on this theme. They differ mainly in the radioligand used for binding studies and in a technique of separation of protein bound from the free moiety. Tritium- -labelled dihydrotestosterone, testosterone and synthetic preparates as methyltrienolone, nandrolone or methandienone were the most frequently used tracers. Using [^{3}H] methyltrienolone (which does not undergo the 5α-reduc- tion), for instance, the relative binding affinities in rat prostate cytosol decreased in the order methyltestosterone - nandrolone - dihydrotestosterone - - 1α-methyldihydrotestosterone - testosterone - methenolone - methandienone - - stanazolol, if we name only the most important ones. A close pattern was obtained in muscle of two species (rats and rabbits) indicating that pro- static as well as muscle cytosol contain the same specific binding entity (ref. 33). The discovery of the gene(s) encoding this (or these) proteins undoubtedly will answer this important question.

The relative binding affinities of various chlorinated anabolics to cytosolic receptor from rat seminal vesicles were studied by Zakár et al. (ref. 34). We have mentioned this and other papers (ref. 35,36) here, since there is discussed the role of a further important factor influencing the over-all activities of androgenic / anabolic steroids in target tissues, i.e. 5α- -reduction. The enzyme (3-oxo-5α-steroid-4-ene dehydrogenase, E.C. 1.3.1.4) is present in prostate and in other male accessory sex organs, but it is almost lacking in muscles of all types. Steroids under consideration may either undergo 5α-reduction as substrates or inhibit its activity. The known differences in "androgenic" and "myotrophic" activities between testosterone and nandrolone may be ascribed to some extent to the action of this enzyme. Both steroids are reduced in prostate to the respective 5α-saturated products, the relative binding affinity to the receptor of which, however, differ considerably. Dihydrotestosterone is well known to possess higher affinity to prostatic receptor than testosterone, whereas the 5α-reduced products of nandrolone are much less active than the parent compound. The importance of the above enzyme in the mechanism of action of androgens and anabolics is documented by numerous studies of its inhibitors (ref. 37).

The availability of androgens or anabolics in target tissues is affected also by other enzymes of degradative steroid metabolism. It should be taken into the account particularly when the strategy of their detection for doping control purposes is to be worked up. The rates of both transport and penetration into the site of action and degradation of steroids in liver is further influenced by their different binding to plasma transport proteins, especially to sex hormone-binding globulin (SHBG). Studies were undertaken to compare the relative binding affinities to SHBG of various androgens and anabolics and the structural requirements for the optimal binding were established (ref. 33,38).

Molecular aspects of endocrine effects of anabolics

The above considerations dealt with the early events of androgen / anabolic action in target cells, i.e. their transport into the cell, their metabolism and binding to specific receptors. Until recently, much less had been known about the action of steroid - receptor complexes on the chromatin, triggering the transcription of genes known to be under steroid hormone control. The methods of molecular biology enable now to find out and describe in terms of nucleotide sequences the genes, encoding various proteins of interest, including those controlled by steroid hormones. It should be emphasized that also steroid receptors themselves do belong to those proteins. So far, most studies have dealt with genes controlled by glucocorticoids (e.g. the gene for tyrosine aminotransferase). The methodological approaches to investigation of steroid hormone receptor - gene interaction may be found in recent reviews (ref. 39,40).

By using the methods of molecular biology so called steroid hormone regulatory elements or steroid responsive elements were revealed. These are nucleotide sequences of approx. 15 base pairs, responsible for binding of steroid - receptor complexes, mediating the triggering and further regulation of the gene expression. These elements are not identical with gene promotors, in fact they were found in the neighbourhood of each flank region of the respective genes (ref. 40,41).

These achievments are challenging since they enable for the first time to elucidate the molecular background of many diverse effects of androgenic / / anabolic steroids in various tissues. Accordingly, their effects on reproduction and growth mentioned in the previous text can be studied now on the level of gene expression. Important questions can be principially answered: Does exist only one gene for androgen / anabolic receptors in secondary sex organs and in muscle? Are there also the regulatory elements interacting in a specific way with these receptors? The growth hormone gene for instance belongs to the genes controlled by glucocorticoids(ref. 37). Do anabolics and androgens influence its expression, too? If so, do the androgen / anabolic receptors bind - completely or partially - to the same regulatory elements as do glucocorticoid - receptor complexes? Does exist some down regulation or androgenic / anabolic receptors in muscle at the level of the gene encoding this receptor? Would it be possible to explain the known excape pheno-menon (i.e. the disappearance of the response to the hormonal stimuli after long term treatment with these drugs) by such mechanism?

We may conclude that the "know how" has been gained and much work has to be done to obtain a deeper insight into the molecular mechanisms responsible for the endocrine effects of anabolic / androgenic steroids. In the following chapter we will return to a more common theme and will try to point to the contribution of the analytical approach, namely immunoassay methods to detection and quantification of anabolics in sportsmen.

TABLE 1. Chemical names of anabolic - androgenic steroids and some other
          hormonal steroids mentioned throughout the text.

Generic or trivial name	Systematic name
Androstanolone	17β-hydroxy-5α-androstan-3-one
Androstenedione	4-androstene-3,17-dione
Androsterone	3α-hydroxy-5α-androstan-17-one
Bolasterone	7α,17α-dimethyl-17β-hydroxy-4-androsten-3-one
Clostebol	4-chloro-17β-hydroxy-4-androsten-3-one
Dehydroepiandrosterone	3β-hydroxy-5-androsten-17-one
Drostanolone	2α-methyl-17β-hydroxy-5α-androstan-3-one
Epitestosterone	17α-hydroxy-4-androsten-3-one
Ethylestrenol	17α-ethyl-4-estren-17β-ol
Etiocholanolone	3α-hydroxy-5β-androstan-17-one
Fluoxymestrone	9α-fluoro-17α-methyl-11β,17β-dihydroxy-4--androsten-3-one
Methandienone	17α-methyl-17β-hydroxy-1,4-androstadien-3-one
Methenolone	1-methyl-17β-hydroxy-5α-androst-1-en-3-one
Methyldihydrotestosterone	17α-methyl-17β-hydroxy-5α-androstan-3-one
Methylnandrolone	17α-methyl-17β-hydroxy-4-estren-3-one
Methyltestosterone	17α-methyl-17β-hydroxy-4-androsten-3-one
Methyltrienolone	17α-methyl-17β-hydroxy-4,9,11-estratrien-3-one
Nandrolone	17β-hydroxy-4-estren-3-one
Norandrosterone	3α-hydroxy-5α-estran-17-one
Nordihydrotestosterone	17β-hydroxy-5α-estran-3-one
Norethandrolone	17α-ethyl-17β-hydroxy-4-estren-3-one
Noretiocholanolone	3α-hydroxy-5β-estran-17-one
Oxandrolone	17α-methyl-17β-hydroxy-2-oxa-5α-androstan-3-one
Oxymetholone	2-(hydroxymethylene)-17α-methyl-17β-hydroxy--5α-androstan-3-one
Stanazolol	17α-methyl-17β-hydroxy-5α-androstano-(3,2C)--pyrazol

IMMUNOASSAY OF ANABOLIC STEROIDS

Introductory remarks

Since anabolics have been listed onto the index of banned drugs in sports,
the ways for their detection have been searched. Radioimmunoassay seems to
be ideal for screening: it is rapid, very sensitive and, predominantly, inexpensive. A series of tens or even hundreds samples can be processed within
one day, depending on automatization facilities. Radioimmunoassay was introduced into steroid analytics surprisingly as late as in 1969, when the
principle of hapten radioimmunoassay had been known and all required materials
and reagents had been avaiable for almost a decade. For instance, the antisera against steroids were prepared by Erlanger et al. as early as in 1957,
originally to be used as antihormones (ref. 43).

The main objection against the use of radioimmunoassay as a single method for
doping control purposes is that it is not able to determine unequivocally the
chemical identity of misused drug. Though group selective, radioimmunoassays
cannot cover all potentially abused drugs (unless the methods for all types
of anabolics have been worked up). Moreover, the sensitivity of radioimmunoassay towards various steroids including the metabolites expected in an
analyzed material vary considerably.

The first radioimmunoassays for two main classes of anabolic steroids, i.e.
17α-methylsteroids and 19-noranalogues of testosterone have been developed
by Brooks et al. (ref. 44) in 1974/1975. A year later these methods were
successfully applied to doping control on Olympic Games 1976 in Montreal
(ref. 45). A remarkable progress of instrumentation in gas chromatography-
-mass spectrometry or mass fragmentometry in the past decade and development
of other chromatographic techniques, especially high performance liquid
chromatography (HPLC), as well as assembling of an impressive collection of
data were probably the main reason that only these techniques have been
designated for official doping control analyses at top sports events. Immunoassays, however, remain very useful for a rapid screening of the presence
of the most frequently used anabolic steroids including testosterone

preparations. They have been used in many national laboratories and also in veterinary medicine or in control of drug residues in food. They are indispensable for pharmacokinetic or excretion studies in patients.

Immunoassay of 17α-methylsteroids

17α-Methylated derivatives of testosterone, dihydrotestosterone and nandrolone represent the largest group of anabolic steroids. The group-selective radioimmunoassay was first developed by Brooks et al. enabling to detect with differentiated sensitivity all steroids possessing the characteristic determinant, i.e. 17ß-hydroxy-17α-methylgroup (ref. 44). Methyltestosterone-3-carboxymethyloxime bovine serumalbumin (BSA) conjugate has been used as an immunogen in rabbits and radioiodinated homologous derivative with tyramine was used as a tracer. The cross-reacting testosterone and other secondary 17ß-hydroxysteroids from urine extract were eliminated by acetylation. The method has been applied among others for the follow up of excretion of stanazolol, perhaps one of the most troublesome anabolic steroids from the analytical point of view (ref. 46).

In our laboratory, we have applied the same immunogen, but we have used tritiated methandienone and, later also directly (i.e. in the steroid nucleus) radioiodinated methandienone as a tracer (ref. 47). The cross reactions with structurally similar hormonal steroids were determined carefully to assess the applicability of the method in doping control. The values obtained with selected 17α-methylsteroids and main potential competitors are shown in Table 2. The variant avoiding extraction was also developed which enabled to shorten the analysis to a few hours. When no exogenous testosterone was present in the analyte, the concentration of cross-reacting unconjugated endogenous testosterone was too low to affect considerably the results. On the other hand, avoiding extraction, the sensitivity decreased markedly so that the requirement for a screening method (a higher sensitivity than that of the method used for a definitive prove of the drug, i.e. GC-MS) was not always fulfilled. As an alternative to RIA we have developed also an enzyme immunoassay for methyltestosterone and related compounds. Using the rabbit antiserum to methyltestosterone-3-carboxymethyloxime:BSA (see Table 2) and horse raddish peroxidase (HRP) as a label we could compare the homologous and bridge heterologous combinations regarding the steroid derivative used for preparation of the tracer. The conjugates of HRP with methyltestosterone-3-carboxymethyloxime and with 17α-methyl-4-androstene-3ß,17ß-diol-3-hemisuccinate were prepared and tested. Surprisingly, better results with respect to binding affinity and ability to be displaced by a non-labelled ligand were obtained using homologous system (ref. 48).

TABLE 2. Cross-reactions of selected steroids with rabbit and goat antibodies against methyltestosterone-3-carboxymethyloxime:
:BSA using [^{3}H]methyltestosterone as radioligand (for systematic names see Table 1)

Steroid	Cross-reaction (%)	
	rabbit	goat
Methandienone	100	100
Methyltestosterone	132	163
Methyldihydrotestosterone	20.2	39.0
Dimethylandrostanolone	16.6	39.5
Stanazolole	5.9	7.2
Fluoxymestrone	4.7	6.5
Oxymetholone	3.2	9.6
Norethandrolone	2.3	5.5
Nandrolone	2.9	1.9
Testosterone	47.6	19.8
Androstanolone	6.9	9.7
Progesterone	0.06	0.13
Estradiol	0.06	0.03

For analytical strategy it is important to know, how anabolics are metabolized in human organism. Though metabolism of the main 17α-methylated anabolics as methyltestosterone, methandienone or stanazolol is known there are still gaps in our knowledge as concerns the less commonly used ones. Methandienone itself, besides the known 6ß-hydroxyderivatives forms also 17ß-methyl-17α--hydroxyepimer ("epimethandienone") (ref. 49). A specific radioimmunoassay has been developed to determine this compound (ref. 50) and it was found that it was excreted in remarkable quantitities following methandienone administration. A typical excretion curve was obtained when both methandienone and its 17-epi-configurated product found in urine were summarized.

Immunoassay of nandrolone and related drugs
The nandrolone 17ß-esters along with testosterone derivatives represent the largest group of parenterally active anabolics. The antisera and ligands to be used for nandrolone radioimmunoassay were prepared at the same time as those for methyltestosterone by Brooks´ group (ref. 44). Homologous (with respect to derivatives used for preparation of the immunogen) radioiodinated derivative with aromatic amines was used as a tracer. The authors summarized the four years experience with practical use of these reagents in   another paper (ref. 51). The antisera against the same immunogen and tritiated nandrolone were used in radioimmunoassay of this drug also in horses (ref.52).

In an attempt to improve the specificity of nandrolone radioimmunoassay, we have raised two antisera with different specificity by combination of two immunogens, differing in the site at the steroid molecule of attachment to the carrier protein. The conjugates on 17ß-hemisuccinate- and 3-carboxy--methyloxime derivatives were synthetized in this case, goats were used for immunization. In keeping with our expectations the antisera recognized the structural details remote from the site of attachment to BSA, i.e. the ring A in the case of 17ß-hemisuccinate derivative and the ring D in the case of 3-oxoderivative. By choosing two model competitors, i.e. 5α-androstane-3α, 17ß-diol as the characteristic cross-reactant with the antiserum against 3-conjugate and androstenedione, cross-reacting considerably with the antiserum against 17ß-conjugate, we were able to determine the optimal composition of the mixture of both antisera, with respect to potential cross-reacting steroids in the analyzed materials. This approach, however, could not avoid the interference of testosterone, possessing both 17ß-hydroxy- and 3-oxogroup. The cross-reactions of selected steroids with both antisera and their mixture are shown in Table 3. [^{3}H]Nandrolone was used as a tracer, but it was demonstrated that directly (i.e. in the steroid nucleus) radioiodinated nandrolone could be used as well (ref. 53).

TABLE 3. Cross-reactions of selected steroids with goat antisera against nandrolone 17ß-hemisuccinate:BSA (A), nandrolone 3-carboxymethyloxime:BSA (B) and with their mixture in optimal ratio (for details see ref. 53)

Steroid	Cross-reaction (%)		
	A	B	A + B
Nandrolone	100	100	100
Nandrolone phenylpropionate	10.1	1.73	5.02
Nordihydrotestosterone	21.4	80.7	27.4
5α-estrane-3ξ,17ß-diol	0.46	20.4	8.26
Methandienone	1.09	0.60	0.97
Testosterone	7.70	6.50	6.90
Dihydrotestosterone	2.06	3.12	2.59
Androstenedione	3.86	0.93	1.83
5α-Androstane-3α,17ß-diol	0.90	6.00	1.01
Epitestosterone	1.98	1.92	1.94
Estradiol	0.38	7.50	0.79
Progesterone	2.13	0.56	1.32

Using the above immunogens and ligands, the assay conditions of nandrolone radioimmunoassay were further studied by Soviet (ref. 54) and Dutch (ref. 55) investigators. The latter authors used a micro-celite chromatography for a complete separation of testosterone, enabling a careful follow up of the pharmacokinetics of nandrolone decanoate, administered to healthy volunteers (ref. 56). In the experiment nandrolone decanoate was released slowly from its deposites by a first order kinetics with a half time approx. 1 week. When entering circulation, however, it was hydrolyzed rapidly with a half time about 1 h. The clearance of free nandrolone displayed a two compartment kinetics with the half times for its distribution and methabolic rate being 10 min and 1 h, respectively.

The pharmacokinetics of nandrolone esters was also investigated in normal men, given nandrolone hexoxyphenylpropionate as an antifertility agent (ref. 11). Testosterone levels were measured, too, both steroids were separated by HPLC prior to radioimmunoassay. During 25 weeks treatment serum nandrolone reached its peak of approx. 20 nmol/l and it sank to one tenth of this concentration within 12 weeks after discontinuation of the steroid intake. Very low nandrolone levels were, however, still detectable even 27 weeks after the drug withdrawal. Using nandrolone radioimmunoassay, we have measured the excretion of two other nandrolone esters, i.e. phenylpropionate and decanoate, respectively, in boys with idiopathic gynecomastia. The apparent excretion half lifes (expressed as the times after which the excreted amount reached one half of its maximal concentration found in urine since discontinuation of treatment) were 2.65 and 4.50 days, respectively (ref. 57). These reports demonstrate a great variability of the rates of absorption and metabolism of nandrolone esters, depending on the application form of the drug and chemical nature of the derivative, and stress the importance of pharmacokinetic and excretion studies.

Nandrolone in the organism is extensively metabolized. Unmetabolized nandrolone in urine amounts usually less than 4 % of administered dose (ref. 21). We have therefore developed a sensitive radioimmunoassay for its main metabolites norandrosterone and noretiocholanolone (ref. 58). For this purpose we have prepared tritium labelled norandrosterone from nandrolone. The synthesis involved oxidation of nandrolone with pyridine chlorochromate, hydrogenation of resulting norandrostenedione with tritium gas under catalysis of tris(triphenylphosphine) rhodium chloride and selective reduction of the 3-oxogroup of $[4,5\alpha-{}^3H]5\alpha$-estrane-3,17-dione with hexachloroiridic acid (ref. 59). For preparation of noretiocholanolone radioligand, the classical two step method consisting of radioiodination of histamine, followed by its attachment to the respective steroid carboxyderivative was used. The immunogens were prepared from 3α-hemisuccinates and 17-carboxymethyloximes of both 19-nor-17-oxosteroids, in view to use the optimal mixture of expected antisera, as in the case of nandrolone. As demonstrated in Table 4, the specificity of the antisera raised by using 17-conjugates was as high that only these antisera were applied for the assay. The method was used for determination of nandrolone metabolites in urine of volunteers obtaining nandrolone phenylpropionate (ref. 48).

TABLE 4.   Cross-reactions of potential steroid competitors with rabbit antisera against 17-carboxymethyloxime:BSA conjugates of norandrosterone and noretiocholanolone (in %)

Steroid competitor	Norandrosterone	Noretiocholanolone
Norandrosterone	100	1.54
Noretiocholanolone	1.02	100
Nandrolone	0.08	0.12
Androsterone	0.77	0.57
Etiocholanolone	0.12	1.29
Testosterone, estradiol, cortisol, progesterone	less than 0.01	

Radioligands used: $[^3H]$Norandrosterone, $[^{125}I]$Iodohistaminylnoretiocholanolone-17--carboxymethyloxime

Detection of testosterone abuse

Since convenient methods have been developed for detection of most synthetic anabolics, the main task for doping control became the abuse of testosterone preparations. Because it is principially impossible to distinguish the exogenous from endogenous hormone by qualitative means, the ways were searched based on quantitative measures.

Brooks et al. (ref. 51) suggested to measure simultaneously testosterone and luteinization hormone (LH) in urine. They demonstrated that when exogenous testosterone was administered, the LH and consequently LH / testosterone ratio was decreased markedly due to a negative feedback mechanism. Extensive studies of excretion of various steroids in thousands of subjects were performed in a number of laboratories. The results were evaluated statistically in order to establish as accurately as possible the statistical variations of steroid concentration in healthy population.

On the base of these studies Donike et al. (ref. 60) showed that 17α-hydroxy-epimer of testosterone (epitestosterone) was excreted by urine in concentrations close to those of testosterone and that its concentration is almost not affected by testosterone intake, probably due to the fact that metabolic degradation of testosterone in liver proceeds much faster than its oxido-reduction on C-17. The measurement of testosterone / epitestosterone ratio has been accepted by official authorities as a tool for the prove of testosterone abuse. Gas chromatography - mass fragmentometry was approved as a method to be used in doping control.

In our laboratory we have developed recently a rapid and sensitive radio-immunoassay of epitestosterone, which in combination with testosterone RIA may be used as an inexpensive screening test for determination of testosterone / epitestosterone ratio in urine (ref. 61). The sample preparation involves an enzymatic hydrolysis of urine followed by direct (non-extraction) assay. The antisera were raised in rabbits by using common 3-carboxymethyl-oxime conjugate as an immunogen and a homologous $[^{125}I]$iodohistaminyl-derivative as a tracer. The specificity of the method is high, as demonstrated in Table 5. The concentrations of both testosterone and epitestosterone in healthy subjects as well as in patients taking testosterone preparations were close to those obtained by other methods, demonstrating the usefulness of this method for screening of testosterone abuse.

TABLE 5. Cross-reactions of selected steroids with rabbit anti-sera against epitestosterone-3-carboxymethyloxime:BSA (for details see ref. 61)

Steroid	Cross-reaction (%)	
Antiserum no.:	2	91
Epitestosterone	100	100
17α-Hydroxy-5α-androstan-3-one	67.2	6.5
Androstenedione	29.6	2.0
4-Androstene-3β,17α-diol	0.04	3.5
Testosterone	0.01	0.1
Nandrolone, methyltestosterone estradiol, progesterone, cortisol	below 0.01	

CONCLUSION

Ethical reasons and the danger side effects of anabolics especially those deteriorating the endocrine regulations and metabolic homeostasis, justify the ban of these drugs in sports. Blacklisting will be effective only if sensitive and specific tests are available for detection of anabolics and their metabolites in biological samples. The forensic character of the doping control in top sport competitions makes steroid analysis in this field extremely responsible and rather difficult. In spite of the fact that GC-MS has been approved as an official method for this purpose, radioimmunoanalytical procedures were further elaborated, to fulfil the requirements for good selectivity and excellent sensitivity and accuracy, to be applied in situations without legal consequences of doping. Such applications may include current doping control during the training course, internal supervision of athletes before competitions, medical research on anabolic drugs, especially their pharmacokinetics and pharmacodynamics and the surveillance of food from animal produce in the market.

REFERENCES

1. A.T. Kenyon, I. Sandiford, A.H. Bryan, K. Knowlton and F.C. Koch, Endocrinology 23, 135-153 (1938).
2. H. Kopera, Acta Endocrin. Suppl. 271, 11-18 (1985).
3. R. Hampl, L. Stárka, J. Heresová, I. Šípová, Z. Pobišová and J. Marek, J. Steroid Biochem. 24, 349-352 (1986).
4. H.L. Kruskemper, Anabolic Steroids, Acad. Pres, New York (1968).
5. J.P. Raynaud and T. Ojasoo, J. Steroid Biochem. 25, 811-833 (1986).
6. R.E. Frisch, A. von Gotz-Welbergen and J.W. McArthur, J. Am. Med. Assoc. 246, 1559-1563 (1981).
7. M.I. Waren, J. Clin. Endocrin. Metab. 51, 1050-1057 (1980).
8. T. Schürmeyer, L. Belkien, U.A. Knuth and E. Nieschlag, Lancet Feb. 25, 417-420 (1984).
9. M. Alén and J. Suominen, Int. J. Sports Med. 5, 189-192 (1984).
10. M. Alén, M.Reivila and R. Vihko, Med. Sci. Sports 17, 354-358 (1985).
11. U.A. Knuth, H. Behre, L.Belkien, H. Bents and E. Nieschlag, Fertil. Steril. 44, 814-821 (1985).
12. R. Hampl, J. Heresová, M. Lachman, J. Šulcová and L. Stárka, Exp. Clin. Endocrin. in press.
13. R. Hampl, J. Zvěřina, J.Šulcová and L. Stárka, Exp. Clin. Endocrin. accepted for publication.
14. L.J.G. Gooren, E.A. van der Veen, H. van Kessel and W. Harmsen-Louman, Andrologia 16, 566-577 (1984).
15. L. Torok, Andrologia 17, 497-501 (1985).
16. C.W. Bardin, J. Endocrin. 117 Suppl., 4 (1988).
17. M. Alén and P. Rahkila, Int. J. Sports Med. 5, 341-342 (1984).
18. J.W.M. Lenders, P.N.M. Demacker, J.A. Vos, P.L.M. Jansen, A.J. Hoitsma, A. van´t Laar and T. Thien, Int.J.Sports Med. 9, 19-23 (1988).
19. E. Eldrup, J. Lindholm and P. Winkel, Clin. Biochem. 20, 105-112 (1987).
20. G.B. Phillips, Am. J. Med. 65, 7-11 (1978).
21. C.D. Kochakian, Anabolic Androgenic Steroids, p.424-425 and 446-449, Springer Verlag, Berlin (1976).
22. L. Lin, G.R. Merriam and R.J. Sherins, J. Clin. Endocrin. Metab. 64, 651-656 (1987).
23. K. Link, R.M. Blizzard, W.S. Evans, D.L. Kaiser, M.W. Parker and A.D. Rogol, J. Clin. Endocrin. Metab. 62, 159-164 (1986).
24. M.W. Parker, A.J. Johanson, A.D. Rogol, D.L. Kaiser and J.M. Blizzard, J. Clin. Endocrin. Metab. 58, 87-90 (1984).
25. I. Parikh, K.G. Rajendran, J.-L. Su, T. Lopez and M. Sar, J. Steroid Biochem. 27, 185-192 (1987).
26. J.M. Gasc and E.E. Baulieu, J. Steroid Biochem. 27, 177-184 (1987).
27. V. Rogozkin, J. Steroid Biochem. 11, 923-926 (1979).
28. G. Michel and E.E. Baulieu, Compt. Rend. Acad. Sci (Paris) 279, 421-424 (1974).
29. J.Y. Dubé, R. Lesage and R.R. Tremblay, Canad. J. Biochem. 54, 50-55 (1976).
30. M. Snochowski, E. Dahlberg and J.A. Gustafsson, Europ. J. Biochem. 111, 603-616 (1980).
31. M. Mayer and F. Rosen, Am. J. Physiol. 229, 1381-1386 (1975).
32. M.A. Ho-Kim, R.R. Tremblay and J.Y. Dubé, Endocrinology 109, 1418-1423 (1981).
33. T. Saartok, E. Dahlberg and J.A. Gustafsson, Endocrinology 114, 2100-2106, (1984).
34. T. Zakár, G. Kaufmann and M. Tóth, Exp. Clin. Endocrin. 87, 133-141 (1986).
35. E.W. Bergink, P.S.L. Janssen, E.W. Turpijn and J. van der Vies, J. Steroid Biochem. 22, 831-836 (1985).
36. M. Tóth and T.Zakár, Exp. Clin. Endocrin. 87, 125-132 (1986).
37. J.R. Brooks, C. Berman, R.L. Primka, G.F. Reynolds and G.H. Rasmusson, Steroids 47, 1-19 (1986).
38. K. Shrimaker, L.J. Salter and R.L.S. Patterson, Horm. Metab. Res. 17, 454-457 (1985).
39. J.H. Winnacker, From Genes to Clones, VCH Publishers (UK), 1987.
40. G. Schütz, Biol. Chem. Hoppe-Seyler 369, 77-86 (1988).
41. M. Beato, J. Arnemann, G. Chalepakis, E.Slater and T.Willmann, J. Steroid Biochem. 27, 9-14 (1987).
42. G.G. Rousseau, P.H. Eliard, J.W. Barlow, F.P. Lemaigre, D.A. Lafontaine, P. De Nayer, I.V. Economidis, P. Formstecher, T. Idziorek., M. Mathy-Hartert, M.L.J. Voz, A. Belayew and J.A. Martial. J. Steroid Biochem. 27, 149-158 (1987).

'43. B.F. Erlanger, F. Borek, S.M. Beiser and S. Lieberman, J.Biol. Chem. 228, 713-727 (1957).

44. R.V. Brooks, R.G. Firth and N.A. Sumner, Brit. J. Sports Med. 9, 89-92, (1975).

45. R. Dugal and M. Bertrand, Analytical Doping Control, Scientific Report, Games of the XXI Olympiad, Montreal, Canada, 1976.

46. O. Lantto, I. Björkhem, H. Ek and D. Johnston, J. Steroid Biochem. 14, 721-727 (1981).

47. R. Hampl, J. Pícha, B. Chundela and L. Stárka, J. Clin. Chem. Clin. Biochem. 16, 279-282 (1978).

48. R. Hampl, M. Bičíková and L. Stárka, Advances in Steroid Analysis '84, p. 219-224, Akadémiai Kiadó, Budapest (1985).

49. H.W. Dürbeck, I. Büker, B.Scheulen and B. Telin, J. Chromatogr. 167, 117-124 (1978).

50. V.Mann, A.B. Benkö and L.T. Kocsár, Steroids 37, 593-600 (1981).

51. R.V. Brooks, G. Jeremiah, W.A. Webb and M. Wheeler, J. Steroid Biochem. 11, 913-917 (1979).

52. W.R. Jondorf, Xenobiotica 7, 671-681 (1977).

53. R. Hampl and L. Stárka, J. Steroid Biochem. 11, 933-936 (1979).

54. V. Rogozkin, V. Morozov and V. Tchaikovsky, Schweiz Z. Sportmed. 27, 169-173 (1979).

55. A.M.G. Bosch, J. Clin. Chem. Clin. Biochem. 22, 22-34 (1983).

56. H.P. Wijnand, A.M.G. Bosch and W. Donker, Acta Endocrin. Suppl. 271, 19-30 (1983).

57. R. Hampl, J. Heresová and L. Stárka, Farmakoterap. Zprávy Spofa (in Czech) 29, 69-77 (1983).

58. R. Hampl, Z. Putz, J. Protiva, J. Filip and L. Stárka, Radiochem. Radioanal. Letters 56, 273-280 (1983).

59. J. Protiva, E. Klinotová, J. Filip and R. Hampl, Radiochem. Radioanal. Letters 53, 277-284 (1982).

60. M.J. Donike, J. Zimmerman, K.R. Bärwald, W. Schänzer, V. Christ, K. Klostermann, and G. Opfermann, Dtsch. Z. Sportmed. 35. 14-24 (1984).

61. R. Bílek, R. Hampl, Z. Putz and L. Stárka, J. Steroid Biochem. 28, 723-729 (1987).

Detection of the administration of natural androgens

R.V. Brooks, A.T. Kicman, N. Poojara and G.J. Southan

United Medical and Dental Schools of Guy's and St Thomas's
Hospitals, London SE1 7EH, England

Abstract - Proof of the administration of hormone drugs can
sometimes be obtained by an examination of the ratios of the
concentrations of hormones or their metabolites excreted in
the urine. Administration of testosterone results in
striking increases in the ratios both of testosterone to
luteinizing hormone and of testosterone to epitestosterone.
In the latter case the value of the test is diminished
because it can be overcome by the normalization of the ratio
by the injection of human chorionic gonadotrophin or by the
administration of testosterone and epitestosterone together
in the appropriate proportion. The administration of another
natural androgen, dihydrotestosterone, can be detected by an
increase in the ratio of dihydrotestosterone to testosterone
and by that of 5α-androstane-3α, 17β-diol to testosterone.

INTRODUCTION

Proof of the administration of endogenous substances from the analysis of
untimed urine collections is inherently difficult to obtain. In the case of
a hormone drug it is sometimes possible to utilise the system controlling the
release of that hormone as an indicator of its administration. The secretion
of testosterone by the testis is stimulated by luteinizing hormone (LH)
secreted by the anterior pituitary. The secretion of LH is, in turn, inhibi-
ted by the circulating testosterone concentration so that there is a homeo-
static mechanism tending to keep the concentration of testosterone constant.
LH also stimulates the testicular secretion of the inactive 17α epimer of
testosterone, epitestosterone. If, therefore, testosterone is administered
to a normal man the endogenous secretion of LH, testosterone and epitestosterone will be suppressed and their excretion in the urine will be diminished.
The excretion of testosterone will increase because of the administration so
that the ratios of testosterone to LH and that of testosterone to epitestosterone will rise.

A test for exogenous testosterone was reported in 1979 based on the testosterone: LH ratio (ref 1) however, when the ban on the use of testosterone was
introduced by the IOC Medical Commission in 1983 it was expressed only in
terms of a testosterone: epitestosterone ratio. This was an unfortunate
decision because it is possible to circumvent a test based on the testosterone: epitestosterone ratio. One way of doing this is to administer human
chorionic gonadotrophin (HCG) a few days before the competition. In the male
HCG has an action identical to that of LH and stimulates the secretion both
of testosterone and epitestosterone. However, unlike LH it is readily available as a pharmaceutical preparation. The result of administering HCG to a
man who has been on testosterone injections is to boost the testosterone
level, declining after the previous injection and at the same time to norma-
lise the testosterone: epitestosterone ratio (ref 2). Despite the similarity
of HCG and LH in respect of biological activity they may be measured specifically by immunoassay procedures using monoclonal antibodies. In 1987 tests
were carried out on 740 urine samples from male sporting events and 21
samples with values in the pregnancy range were found.

A second possible method of overcoming the testosterone: epitestosterone ratio test would be to inject not the testosterone ester alone but in combination with the corresponding epitestosterone ester. Wilson and Lipsett reported that although normal males excrete approximately equal amounts of the two epimers in the urine, the secretion rate of the 17β epimer is some 30 times greater than that of the 17α (ref 3). The heptanoate of epitestosterone has therefore been synthesised and injected with that of testosterone in a ratio of 1:30.

EXPERIMENTAL

Epitestosterone was converted to the heptanoate (ref 4) purified by chromatography on alumina columns and TLC and dissolved in Primoteston (R) for sterile injection.

A normal male was given a simple injection of Primoteston (R) (250 mg) and the urine collected for 1 day before and 10 days following the injection. Some months later the same subject was injected with the combined injection containing the heptanoates of testosterone and epitestosterone and the same urine collections made. The concentrations of LH , testosterone and epitestosterone in the urine were measured by radioimmunoassay (ref 2).

Results
The upper part of Fig 1 shows the effect on the two ratios of administering testosterone heptanoate alone. Both ratios increase rapidly and exceed the interrupted horizontal line representing the cut-off point for the two assays at 5 standard deviations above the mean for normal subjects transformed to give a normal distribution. In the lower part of the figure, following the administration of the 17β and 17α esters in a ratio of 30:1, only the testosterone: LH ratio rises. This demonstrates that it is possible to escape detection of testosterone doping if the test used is based on the ratio testosterone: epitestosterone.

DETECTION OF DIHYDROTESTOSTERONE

In most androgen target tissues testosterone is converted by a 5α-reductase enzyme to dihydrotestosterone (DHT) which has a greater affinity for the androgen receptor than testosterone. Conversion of DHT back to testosterone is not possible although some further reduction to 5α-androstane-3α, 17β-diol (3αdiol) occurs. Since administration of DHT suppresses the secretion of testosterone (ref 4) it would seem that a detection system based on the urinary ratios of DHT: testosterone and of the 3α-diol: testosterone might be effective.

Experimental
Dihydrotestosterone heptanoate was synthesised by the method of Keenan et al (ref 4) purified by chromatography on a column alumina and by recrystallisation and administered by intramuscular injection in sesame oil.

Urine samples were hydrolysed with β-glucuronidase, the steroid fraction extracted with ethylene dichloride and separated into testosterone, DHT and 3α diol fractions on reverse phase HPLC. Each of these fractions was quantitated by radioimmunoassay using an antiserum raised to 5α-androstane-3α, 17β-diol-7-0-carboxymethyloxime coupled to bovine serum albumin. The assay used $[1,2-^3H]$-3αdiol as tracer and separated bound and free analyte fractions with dextran coated charcoal. The cross-reactions against 3α diol standards were: testosterone 50%, DHT 150%.

Results
A normal male given an injection of 150 mg DHT heptanoate gave the results shown in Fig 2. The testosterone: epitestosterone and the testosterone: LH ratios shown in the upper part of Fig 2, did not rise. The cut-off level for these ratios is indicated by the interrupted horizontal line. The ratios of 3α diol: testosterone and of DHT: testosterone rise rapidly from the values for the two basline urines. It is evident that the heptanoate of DHT is released from the site of injection much more slowly than that of testosterone. The 3αdiol: testosterone ratio does not decrease below 5 until day 15 and returns to basal values on day 27. Weekly injections of DHT heptanoate would therefore by expected to result in a summation of values and a greater ease of detection. Twenty four normal males gave a 3α diol: testosterone value of 2.0 ± 0.9 s.d. For the DHT x 10: testosterone ratio the mean was 5.0 ± 2.8 s.d.

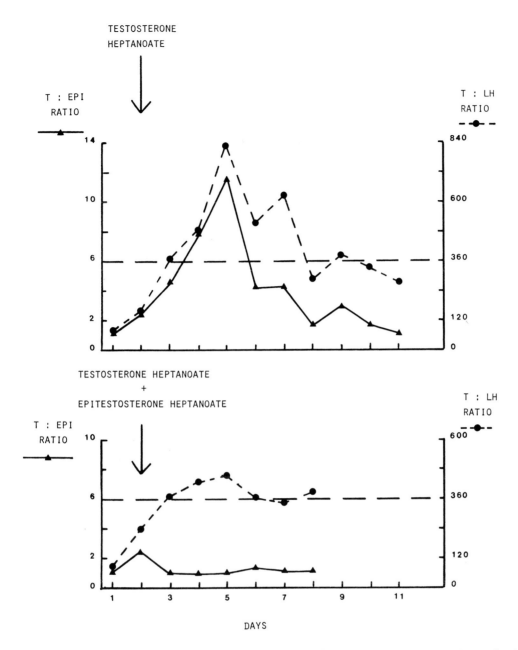

Fig 1. Normalization of the testosterone: epitestosterone (T:EPI) ratio by the administration of both steroids together.

   The interrupted horizontal lines represent the cut-off point for the two ratios (testosterone: epitestosterone = 6.0, testosterone: LH = 360)

   CONCLUSIONS

The administration of the heptanoate of dihydrotestosterone can be detected by the elevation of the 3α diol: testosterone ratio in the urine. The DHT x 10: testosterone ratio, although more variable, may give useful confirmation.

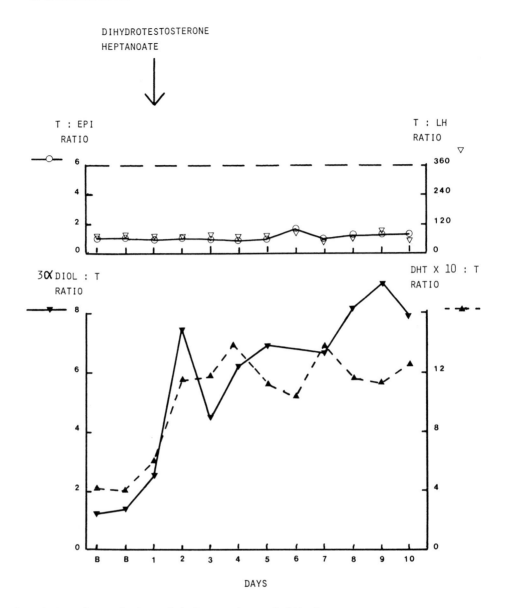

Fig 2.   Detection of the administration of dihydrotestosterone.

REFERENCES

1. R.V. Brooks, G. Jeremiah, W.A. Webb and M. Wheeler, J. Steroid Biochem. 11, 913-917 (1979).
2. R.V. Brooks, A.T. Kicman, N.S.E. Nanjee and G.J. Southan, Proceedings 12th International Congress of Clinical Chemistry, Rev. Bras. Anal. Chem. 6, 109 (1984).
3. H. Wilson and M.B. Lipsett, J. Clin. Endocr. 26, 902-914 (1966).
4. B.S. Keenan, A.J. Eberts, J.T. Sparrow, N.G. Greger and W.B. Panko, J. Clin. Endocrinol. Metab. 64, 557-562 (1987).

The detection of synthetic and natural corticosteroids

G.J. Southan and R.V. Brooks

United Medical and Dental Schools of Guy's and St Thomas's
Hospitals, London SE1 7EH, England

Abstract - The synthetic corticosteroids dexamethasone and
prednisolone, can be detected in urine up to 24 hours after
a single oral dose of 2 mg and 5 mg respectively, by a single
radioimmunoassay (RIA) screen. In the case of the principal
naturally occurring human corticosteroid, cortisol, its concentration, and that of its metabolites were measured against
the concentrations of adrenal androgen metabolites to provide
an index for cortisol doping.

INTRODUCTION

Corticosteroids have been on the IOC list of banned substances since 1986 and
while the approach to testing for the synthetic corticosteroids is straight-
forward, in that the presence of the steroid or its metabolites in the urine
sample is proof of administration, the testing for naturally occurring
cortisol must rely on indices other than cortisol concentration alone.

Cortisol is secreted by the adrenal gland, under the control of ACTH released
from the anterior pituitary (Fig 1). Cortisol feeds back on the anterior
pituitary to inhibit ACTH release, and this negative feedback loop controls
the level of circulating cortisol. Administration of cortisol will, therefore, inhibit the release of ACTH. Unfortunately, it is not possible to use
a urinary cortisol: ACTH ratio as an index of cortisol doping because of the
instability of ACTH. However, inhibition of ACTH reduces the secretion, not
only of cortisol, but also that of the adrenal androgens, which are also
under ACTH control (Fig 1). That is, cortisol administration indirectly
suppresses adrenal androgens.

DHA and DHA sulphate are androgens of predominantly adrenal origin and are
excreted, in part, as DHA sulphate. The urinary cortisol: DHA sulphate ratio
would, therefore, be expected to increase after the ingestion of cortisol.
11β-hydroxy androstenedione is of exclusive adrenal origin. It is excreted
in urine as the 11β-hydroxy 17-oxo steroids 11β-hydroxy androsterone (5α),
11β-hydroxy aetiocholanolone (5β) and, to a lesser extent, the related 11-
oxo 17-oxo steroids (5α and 5β) (ref 1). These four compounds also arise
from cortisol metabolism, accounting for about 5% of secreted cortisol. But,
whereas cortisol gives predominantly the 5β isomers, 11β-hydroxy androstenedione gives mainly the 5α isomers. Exogenous cortisol would increase the
proportion of the 5β isomers found, at the same time reducing the 5α contribution of 11β-hyroxy androstenedione by suppressing its adrenal production.
Both effects would be expected to increase the 5β: 5α ratio.

The relative contributions of cortisol and 11β-hydroxy androstenedione to the
5β and 5α metabolites were examined by suppressing the normal adrenal production of both, by taking 1 mg dexamethasone at midnight and ingesting 20 mg of
either cortisol or 11β-hydroxy androstenedione nine hours later. The
measured 5β: 5α ratio of the 11 oxygenated 17-oxo steroids is then assumed to
be predominantly from the ingested steroid.

One of the physiological responses to stress, including vigorous exercise, is
the increased secretion of ACTH. To mimick this effect synthetic ACTH was
injected.

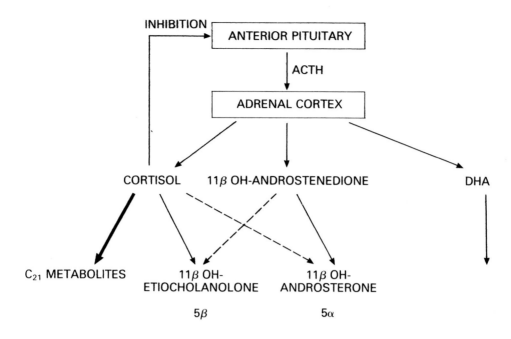

Fig 1.   Metabolites of Adrenocortical Steroids.

In view of the adrenal suppression caused by taking corticosteroids, the amount of corticosteroid ingested must be at least equivalent to the cortisol production that is being suppressed. The normal cortisol secretion rate is around 20 mg per day so the minimum dose of prednisolone, which is five times as potent a glucocorticoid as cortisol, would be 5 mg. Dexamethasone is even more potent, and the equivalent dose is 2 mg.

EXPERIMENTAL

Synthetic corticosteroids
5 mg prednisolone was given orally to 7 subjects and urine collected from 0-8 hrs, 8-24 hrs and 24-48 hrs post administration. 2 mg dexamethasone was given orally to 4 volunteers and similar urine saves made.

Urinary concentrations of prednisolone were estimated by RIA, using antisera raised to prednisolone-21-hemisuccinate-BSA with the following cross-reactions: dexamethasone 2.5%; cortisol 6.7%. Dexamethasone concentrations were estimated using antisera raised to dexamethasone-21-hemisuccinate-BSA giving cross-reactions of 2.5% with prednisolone and 1.4% with cortisol.

Cortisol
The following protocol was observed:

Day	Time	
1		control
	2400	oral dexamethasone 1 mg
2	0900	oral cortisol 20 mg
	2400	oral dexamethasone 1 mg
3	0900	oral 11β-hydroxy androstenedione 20 mg
8	0900	Synacthen 0.5 mg depot
15	0900	oral cortisol 20 mg

Urine collections made from 0900-2100 hrs on each day.

Urinary measurements
Urinary free cortisol was measured by direct RIA (Immunodiagnostics kit). DHA-SO$_4$ concentrations were estimated by RIA following a C18 solid phase extraction. 11β-hydroxy 17-oxo steroids and 11-oxo 17-oxo steroids were extracted using solid phase C18 and NH columns and ratios estimated by GLC on a DB1 fused silica capillary column (30m, J & W Scientific, Inc). 11β-hydroxy 17-oxo steroids were run as trimethylsilyl ethers/enol ethers. Selective oxidation of the 11β-hydroxy group to an 11-oxo group, following acetylation and oximation, meant that the 5β: 5α ratio of the total 11 oxygenated (i.e. 11β-hydroxy + 11-oxo) 17-oxo steroids could be estimated.

RESULTS

Synthetic corticosteroids

Urine excreted in the 48 hours after the administration of 2 mg dexamethasone gave an RIA titre corresponding to 2.4 ± 0.5% (mean ± SEM) of the dose of steroid. In the case of prednisolone the urine titre was equivalent to 7.8 ± 0.4% of the 5 mg dose. Only 0.5% of secreted or administered cortisol is excreted unchanged in the urine. The higher proportion excreted in the free fraction for the synthetic corticosteroids is probably due to the extra double bond in the 1.2 position preventing A ring reduction which is the principal metabolic pathway for cortisol. Because of the greater proportion excreted unchanged, 5 mg prednisolone, taken orally, will give a high value on the dexamethasone assay for up to 24 hours, even though the prednisolone cross-reaction is low. This allows a single RIA screen to be used for both dexamethasone and prednisolone.

The majority of the unchanged steroid excreted is during the first 8 hours (prednisolone 84.0 ± 8% (mean ± SEM) dexamethasone 68.5 ± 12%) and the concentration of subsequent urine saves will rapidly decline until they are no longer discernible from normal "blank" urines. This is because of the cross-reaction with cortisol, which is excreted continually throughout the day. However, there are several methods of minimising the interference due to cortisol. The cross-reaction (1.4%) can be reduced to 0.2% by preincubating the assay with stripped pregnancy plasma so that the protein, cortisol binding globulin (CBG), contained in it, will bind to the cortisol and prevent its interference in the assay (ref 2). However, prednisolone binds to CBG and its cross reaction is also reduced. Using a more specific binding protein, i.e. a cortisol antiserum, produced little benefit. Adding cortisol itself to the assay tubes to saturate those binding sites in the polyclonal antibody with a high affinity for cortisol, caused a reduction in the cortisol cross reaction, but at the expense of reduced binding of the label so that some sensitivity was lost (ref 2). However, background levels for normal urines fell and allowed lower levels of synthetic corticoids to be picked up.

Selective reaction of Girard reagent T (trimethyl-aminoacetohydrazide hydroxychloride) with the 3-oxo-4-ene group of cortisol in preference to the 3-oxo-1, 4-diene system of prednisolone and dexamethasone, prior to the assay, provides a method of converting cortisol to a non-immunoreactive derivative (ref 3) and reducing the cross reaction (0.1%). Dexamethasone and prednisolone are only slightly affected. Using this method the second 24 hour save for dexamethasone can be shown as "positive" at concentrations of 500 pg/ml urine.

For samples that are suspect on the initial screen, HPLC followed by RIA can be used as a second stage to identify the cross-reacting species; fractions corresponding to various drugs can be collected from the HPLC and reassayed using the relevant antiserum and their concentration estimated. It may even be desirable to use the prednisolone specific assay before HPLC as the size of the response compared to that of the dexamethasone assay gives an indication of the steroid present. The HPLC conditions can then be optimised for the steroid thought to be present. This approach has been extended to include related steroids such as betamethasone, 6 -methyl prednisolone and beclomethasone.

Cortisol

In all subjects urinary free cortisol excretion increased after taking cortisol and in some cases DHA sulphate excretion decreased. This resulted in a large increase in the cortisol: DHA sulphate ratio after cortisol ingestion in each individual (Fig 2). The usefulness of this increase as an indicator of cortisol doping is severely limited by the wide range of basal values. The high ratios for the basal urines were due to low DHA sulphate concentrations rather than high cortisol values. Some subjects showed low values of urinary DHA sulphate that changed little with ACTH stimulation or dexamethasone suppression, whereas their corresponding plasma values showed the expected responses. This suggests that differences in metabolism of DHA and DHA sulphate may be responsible for the wide variation in basal urinary DHA sulphate concentrations. The lowest mean cortisol: DHA sulphate ratio was for the second day of dexamethasone suppression and the greatest after ACTH stimulation (Table 1). This may be due, in part, to the low clearance rate of DHA sulphate from plasma blunting the response of urinary DHA sulphate to these changes.

TABLE 1.   Response of cortisol: DHA sulphate and 5β : 5α 11β-hydroxy-17 oxo steroid ratios to treatment.

Treatment	Cortisol: DHA sulphate ratio			11β hydroxy-17 oxo steroid 5β: 5α ratio		
	mean	SD	Range	mean	SD	Range
Dexamethasone 11 hydroxy androstenedione	2.5	3.7	0.4-12.3	0.3	0.2	0.1-0.6
Normal	7.9	12.7	0.4-41.0	1.0	0.5	0.4-1.8
ACTH	66.7	89.0	6.5-289	1.5	1.3	0.2-4.3
Cortisol	49.7	32.5	6.5-88.8	5.7	3.4	2.2-12
Dexamethasone cortisol	36.4	31.8	5.4-93.5	10.0	12.9	1.7-43

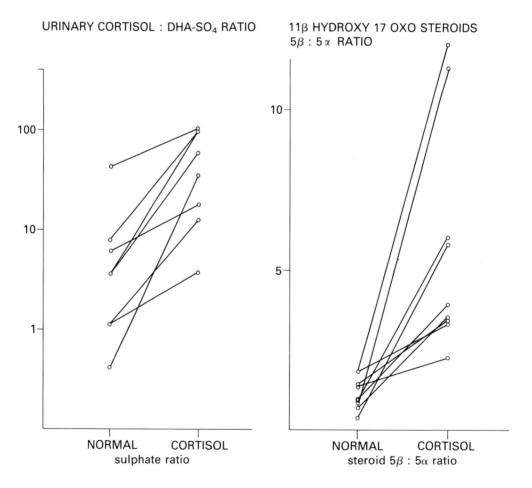

Fig 2.

The mean 11β-hydroxy 17-oxo steroid 5β: 5α ratio showed an increase over the basal levels when cortisol had been administered and a decrease when 11 - hydroxy androstenedione had been taken (Table 1). This illustrates the general increase in the 5β: 5α ratio corresponding to an increase in the expected contribution from cortisol. Measurement of the 11-oxo 17-oxo steroids with 11β- hydroxy 17-oxo steroids caused a greater spread of values for the basal day and a more varied response to the various treatments. ACTH caused only a small increase in the mean 5β: 5α ratio, implying that over the time period studied any differential response of cortisol and adrenal androgens to adrenal stimulation is not important. Although there is no overlap of basal and cortisol administration groups for the 11β- hydroxy 17-oxo steroids (Fig 3), only a small number of subjects (9) were studied. Any cut off point above which it is deemed cortisol doping to have taken place would have to be based on a much larger population. However, from these results it would appear that such a cut off level would exclude some subjects taking cortisol. On the other hand, the amount administered in this study is probably the minimum effective dose and much larger doses would probably be used by an athlete.

CONCLUSION

The screen for the synthetic corticosteroids is sensitive enough to detect, on the day, administration of a relatively small dose of dexamethasone or prednisolone. HPLC and further RIA can identify which drug is being used and give an estimate of its concentration. Final confirmation is by GC/MS.

The cortisol: DHA sulphate ratio was found to be unsuitable as an index of cortisol doping due to the variation in normal DHA sulphate excretion. Although the 5β: 5α 11 -hydroxy 17-oxo steroid ratio may be useful as such an index, it may be desirable to supplement it with other indices such as the ratio of the tetrahydro metabolites of cortisol to the sum of androsterone and aetiocholanolone.

REFERENCES

1. H.L. Bradlow and T.F. Gallagher, J. Biol. Chem. 229, 505-518 (1957).
2. J.J. Pratt and M.G. Woldring, Clin. Chem. Acta 68, 87-90 (1976).
3. J.C.K. Loo, A.B. Vilim, N. Jordan and J. Moffat, Journal of Pharmaceutical Sciences 65, 461-462 (1976).

The potential applications of an androgenic receptor assay for anabolic steroid screening

Robin A. Felder, Marilyn Hamilton, William Geary

Department of Pathology, The University of Virginia Health Sciences Center, Charlottesville, VA 22908

INTRODUCTION

There is widespread use of anabolic steroids by athletes in an attempt to improve athletic performance. The use of anabolic steroids for performance enhancement has been banned by most athletic organizations throughout the world. Enforcement of the ban on anabolic steroids has relied on the testing of athlete urine for the presence of exogenously administered anabolic steroids. The use of radioimmunoassay to screen athlete urine for exogenously administered steroids demonstrates a lack of sensitivity for many synthetic steroids. Furthermore, screening for synthetic testosterone, 17 alpha-methyl steroid, and 19 nor-steroid use requires three separate RIA procedures. It is now generally agreed that gas chromatography coupled with mass spectrometry (GCMS) is the method of choice for screening for steroid abuse. GCMS, however, is plagued by the large initial investment for equipment and the slow laborious nature of the analysis.

For athletes, the target of natural and synthetic steroids are muscular androgen receptors, which when stimulated are purported to promote protein synthesis and muscle growth. Androgen receptors will bind natural and synthetic steroids with affinities proportional to their anabolic activities. Radioreceptor assays in the past have provided a convenient, rapid and cost effective means to quantitate compounds in a variety of biological systems including atrial natriuretic factor in serum (1) and neuroleptics in serum (2). We therefore investigated the use of a radioreceptor assay using rat ventral prostate (a rich source of androgen receptors) and mibolerone (7 alpha-dimethyl-19 nortestosterone) to quantitate androgenic compounds in urine from normal subjects and athletes who were excreting exogenously administered androgenic steroids.

MATERIALS AND METHODS

Materials - Mibolerone (M) and (3H)-Mibolerone (3H-M) (7 alpha, 17 dimethyl-17beta-hydroxy-4-estren-3-one) were purchased from New England Nuclear (Boston, Ma). All other steroids were purchased from Steraloids (Wilton, N.H.). TES buffer consisted of the following components: TES, 10 mM, (Sigma cat# T-1375), EDTA-disodium, 1.5 mM, (Fisher Scientific, cat# S-311), sucrose, 250 mM, (Fisher Scientific, cat# S-5), molybdate-sodium salt, 20 mM, (Sigma, ca# M-1003), monothioglycerol, 12 mM, (Sigma, cat# M-1753). The above reagents were added to 800 mL of deionized water and mixed until dissolved. Proteolytic enzyme inhibitors were added by dissolving in 10 mg iodoacetamide (Sigma, cat# I-6125), (caution, light sensitive) and 10 mg PMSF (Sigma, cat# P-7626) in 250 µL of absolute ethanol and adding it all at once to rapidly mixing TES buffer. The buffer was then adjusted to one liter and pH 7.4 at 4C. Bound was separated from free steroid with dextran coated charcoal. A 1% Dextran T-70 solution containing 0.15% gelatin, 1.5 mM EDTA and 50 mM TRIS, pH 7.4 at 23C, was used to suspend washed and dried charcoal to a final concentration of 1%. Sodium acetate buffer (1.1 M) and beta-glucuronidase (Sigma, cat# G-0876) were prepared for urine hydrolysis (Fisher Scientific, cat# S-210).

Urinary steroid samples-Random morning urine samples were obtained from
normal subjects and athletes who admitted taking steroids. The presence of
exogenously administered steroids in the athletes was confirmed by gas
chromatography-mass spectrometry.

Tissue preparation - Wistar Kyoto Rats (WKY) served as the source of ventral
prostatic tissue. The rats were kept on a standard Purina chow with
adlibitum access to water. The rats were sacrificed by decapitation following which the ventral prostate (highest concentration of androgen receptors)
was quickly removed and placed in chilled TES buffer. The rat prostates were
minced to a fine paste using a razor blade on a chilled glass plate. Approximately 6 mL TES buffer was used to suspend the minced tissue in a round
bottomed test tube. The minceate was then homogenized in a Polytron (Tekmar
Co., Cincinnate, OH) at a setting of 50 for 4 x 15 second bursts with a 30
second rest on ice between each burst. The honogenate was then centrifuged
in a prechilled Ti75 rotor for one hour at 42,000 RPM at 4C. The supernatant
was then separated from the lipid layer and stored on ice until assay within
one hour.

Preparation of urinary steroids - Urinary steroids are generally excreted a
glucuronidase due to metabolism. Sugar moieties were removed though the use
of a glucuronidase enzyme preparation to release the free steroids (56C for
one hour).

Solid phase extraction columns (C-18 Sep-Pak, Waters Assoc., Milford, MA)
were prepared by washing with 10 mL deionized water followed by 20 mL HPLC
grade methanol, followed by 10 deionized water, followed by 20 ml air.
Normal or athlete urine (10 mL) was slowly pushed through the column using a
plastic syringe. The column was washed with 10 mL deionized water and dried
with 20 mL air. Steroids were eluted with 2 mL methanol and dried under
nitrogen at 40C. The steroids were then reconstituted with 1.1 M acetate
buffer and hydrobysed for 1 hour at 56C or overnight at 37C. The cooled
tubes were subjected to one additional column extraction by the dried extract
was reconstituted with 10 mL TTESM buffer. The samples were then mixed for 1
hour at 25C and then stored at 4C until assay.

Preparation of Testosterone Standards - A stock testosterone standard (1mg/ml)
was prepared using absolute ethanol. The stock standard was stable at 0C for
6 months. A working standard curve was generated which covered the range of
10 µM to 10 pM in TES buffer by doing serial 1:10 dilutions.

Radio-receptor assays - All tubes were chilled in an ice water bath before
the start of the binding experiment. Using an Eppendorf repeating pipette
100 µl buffer (0 standard), standards and samples were placed in appropriately labeled tubes. 3H-M was then added followed by chilled prostatic tissue
to commence the binding reaction. After 35 minutes incubation 400 µl of cold
charcoal suspension was added to all tubes. After ten minutes the samples
were centrifuged in a prechilled Beckman TJ-6 rotor at 3,000 RPM for 20
minutes. An aliquot of the supernatant was counted in a scintillation vial
with 15 mL scintillation fluid.

        RESULTS

The binding of 3H-M to the cytosolic fraction of rat ventral prostate was
saturable with respect to time. 3H-M reached steady state in 30 minutes at
35nM 3H-M at 0C (data not shown), therefore 30 minute incubations were used
throughout all experiments. The ability of testosterone and unlabelled M to
compete for 3H-M binding in rat ventral prostate cytosol was tested (Fig 1).
3h-M binding to prostate receptor was strongly competed by other anabolic
androgens but not by non-androgenic steroids (estrogen, androsterone, and
cortisol) (Fig 2). The inhibitory constants for these compounds were calculated according to Cheng and Prusoff (3) (Table 1). 3H-M binding to rat
ventral prostate cytosol was analyzed according to the method of Scatchard as
modified by Rosenthal (4) (Fig 3). The dissociation constant (Kd) was 1.1+/-
0.2 nM and maximal receptor density was 7.4 +/-6.8 pmol/mg protein.

Urine prepared according to the procedure described in Materials and Methods
were tested for their ability to compete for 3H-M binding to rat prostate
(Fig 4). The urinary extracts prepared from normal subjects were less potent
in their ability to compete for 3H-M binding when compared to athletes who
were on high daily intades of anabolic steroids. All athletes were ingesting
at least 10 mg of either Anaver, Durobolin, or Deca Durobol daily for over 10
weeks prior to analysis. There was no difference in the ability of athlete
urine containing 17 alpha-methyl steroids compared to 19 nor-steroids to

TABLE 1

Steroid	Ki(nM)	SE	N
Mibolerone	2.0	0.18	3
17 a-meth	1.5	0.92	3
19 nor	1.2	0.50	3
Testosterone	10.4	2.1	4

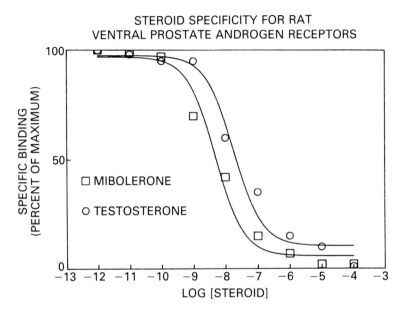

Fig 1. The ability of either testosterone or Mibolerone to compete for [3H]-M (1nM) binding was examined. Non-specific binding was determined in the presence of 1 µM testosterone. Ki values are listed in table 1.

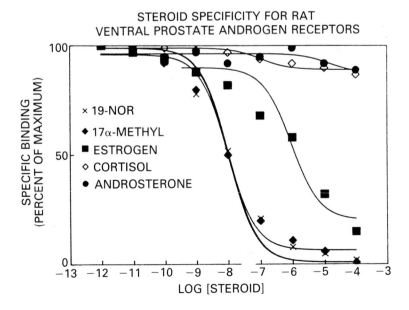

Fig 2. The ability of non-anabolic steroids and 17 alpha-methyl (17beta-hydroxy 17alpha-methyl 4-androsten-3-one) and 19-nor (4-androstene-19-nor 17beta-ol-3-one) steroids to compete for [3H]-M binding was determined. The ki values are listed in table 1.

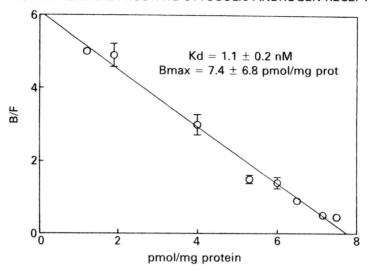

SCATCHARD PLOT OF [³H]-MIBOLERONE BINDING
TO RAT VENTRAL PROSTATE CYTOSOLIC ANDROGEN RECEPTOR

$Kd = 1.1 \pm 0.2$ nM
$Bmax = 7.4 \pm 6.8$ pmol/mg prot

Fig 3.   Scatchard analysis of 3H-M binding to rat ventral prostate cytosol. Cytosol was incubated in TES buffer containing 3H-M and either buffer alone (total binding) or buffer containing 1 μM testosterone (non-specific binding).

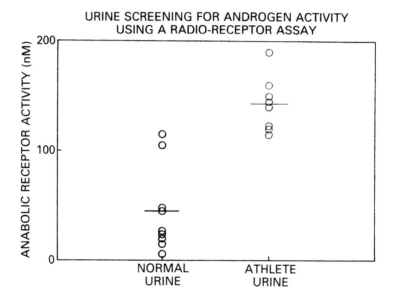

URINE SCREENING FOR ANDROGEN ACTIVITY
USING A RADIO-RECEPTOR ASSAY

Fig 4.   Urinary extracts prepared from normal subjects were less potent in their ability to compete for 3H-M binding when compared to athletes who were on high daily intakes of anabolic steroids (normal mean = 45 +/- 15.2, Mean +/- SEM, N=9, p 0.005, athlete mean = 143 +/- 8.5, N=8).

compete for 3H-M binding. Normal urinary steroids demonstrated a wide variability in their affinity for the rat prostate steroid receptor yet they were less potent than athlete urinary steroids. Urine from athletes which were on a low steroid consumption (i.e. a single dose) were not tested. Similarly the correlation between amount of steroid use and the ability to compete for 3H-M binding was not tested due to the difficulty in obtaining accurate data about steroid consumption from athletes and the random nature of the urine collection.

The stability of prepared cytosol was tested by measuring the ability of Mibolerone to compete for (3H)-M binding in freshly prepared rat ventral prostate cytosol compared to cytosol which had been frozen in TES buffer at 80C overnight (Fig 5). There was a 50% decrease in specific [3H]-M binding in frozen cytosol, therefore fresh preparations were used for all experiments.

Since the stability of cytosolic preparations precludes it from routine clinical use, we examined the binding of M to coverslip mounted prostate sections. The specific binding of (3H)-M to coverslip mounted frozen sections of rat prostate was 50-60% of total binding. Specific binding was also time dependant, linear with tissue receptor concentrations, and saturable. Saturation studies with 0.5-2.0 nM (3H)-M using 20, 40, and 60 minute incubation times showed saturable binding at all 3 time points (Fig 6A). Eadie-Hofstee analysis of these studies yielded Kd estimates of 0.22-0.24 nM. (3H)-M binding was also saturable with respect to time with steady state occurring at 30 minutes (Fig 6B). After 60 minutes there was a progressive decay of binding suggesting either ligand degradation or loss of nuclear bound receptor to the incubation medium.

DISCUSSION

Screening assays for drugs of abuse have been developed for many compounds which have been banned by athletic organizations because of their ability to enhance athletic performance. The ability to detect anabolic steroids has lagged behind other drugs of abuse because of the wide variety of steroid analogues which have anabolic activity has hampered assay development. Radioimmunoassays (RIA) were developed which detected the main anabolic steroids used by athletes (5). The specificity of antisera, however, prohibits one RIA from detecting all steroids. Radioreceptor assays are particularly useful where quantitation of a class of compounds with common activities. For example, calf caudate dopamine-2 receptors are used to quantitate many structurally unrelated neuroleptics since their ability to bind to dopamine-2 receptors is proportional to their neuroleptic activity.

In these studies we prepared a radioreceptor assay using 3H-M and cytosolic steroid receptors from rat ventral prostate. Mibolerone has been widely used in the quantitation of androgen receptors because it is stable to metabolism in cellular honogenates, does not bind appreciable to sex hormone binding globulin, has a high affinity (1 nM) for the androgen receptor found in prostatic tissue, has a low affinity for the progesterone receptor, and is both a 17 alpha-methyl and 19 nor-testosterone derivative (6). M is particularly useful to serve as a radioligand in these assays because it possesses structural similarities to all classes of steroids abused by athletes.

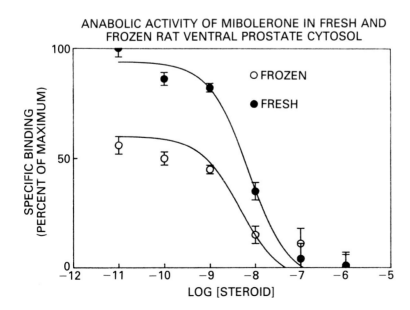

Fig 5.   Freshly prepared rat ventral prostate cytosol was compared to frozen cytosol in its ability to bind [3H]-M. Frozen cytosol showed a diminished ability to bind [3H]-M.

A

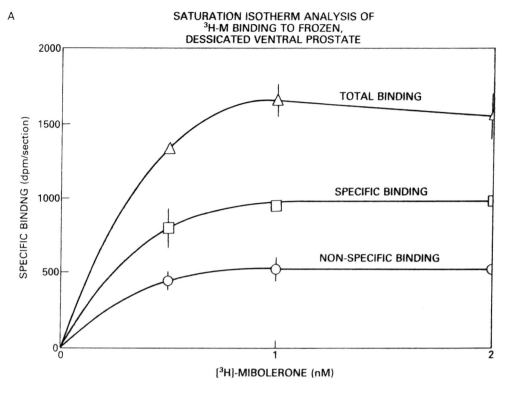

B

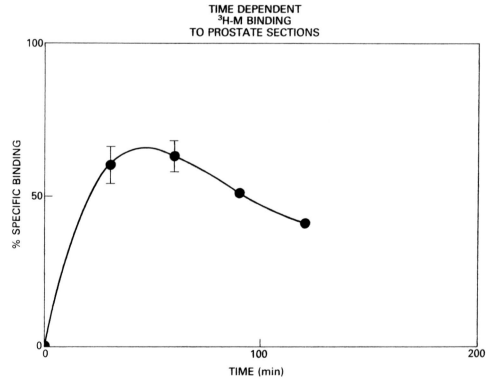

Fig 6A. Saturation isotherm analysis of [3H]-M binding to rat ventral
        prostate frozen sections after 20, 40, and 60 minutes of incubation.
        Specific binding was determined by concurrent incubations of sections
        with 1 µM testosterone. Data is presented as mean of X +/- range for
        duplicate experiments.
Fig 6B. Time dependent binding of [3H]-M to rat ventral prostate frozen
        sections. Saturation occurred after 30 minutes of binding but
        decayed after 60 minutes. Data is presented as the mean of X +/-
        range for duplicate experiments.

Results of these studies demonstrate that the prostate steroid receptor can differentiate quantitative differences in 3H-M binding between normal and athlete urine. It is presumed that the binding differences are a result of the presence of exogenous steroids administered by the athletes since synthetic steroids were detect in these specimens by gas chromatography mass spectrometry. All of the athletes tested using the radio-receptor assay demonstrated high amounts of anabolic receptor activity which was equal to that of the two lowest athletes. In this configuration of the radio-receptor assay, false positive results would be confirmed by gas chromatography mass spectrometry. It remains to be determined if urine samples from athletes who are on low dose steroids or those who have recently discontinued their use can still be detected.

The use of labile homogenates of rat ventral prostate does not make this assay suitable for most clinical or commercial laboratory environments. In preliminary studies we have demonstrated that 10 μm frozen desiccated sections from rat ventral prostate could also be used as a quantitative radio-receptor assay. The desiccated sections can be stored for up to a year at -80C with no loss of binding activity. Since the frozen sections can be affixed to the end of slender glass slide, a radioreceptor "dip-stick" assay could be developed with the stability necessary for the clinical laboratory environment.

In conclusion, the radioreceptor assay for anabolic steroids has the potential of filling the need for a single, low cost, and rapid assay that can screen for all anabolic steroids in human urine in proportion to their activities. Confirmation can then be subsequently performed by GCMS.

BIBLIOGRAPHY

1. Ballerman B. A highly sensitive radioreceptor assay for ANP in rat plasma. Amer. S. Physiol. 254, F159-F163, 1988.
2. Tune L.E. and Coyle J.T. Neuroleptic drug level monitoring in psychiatry: Focus on radioreceptor assay techniques. Therapeutic Drug Monitoring 4, 59-64, 1982.
3. Cheng Y.C. and Prusoff W.H. Relationship between the inhibition constant (Ki) and the concentration of inhibitor which causes 50 percent inhibition (IC) of an enzymatic reaction. Biochem. Pharmacol. 22, 3099-310, 1973.
4. Rosenthal H.E. A graphic method for the determination and presentation of binding parameters in a complex system. Anal. Biochem. 20, 525-532,
5. Brooks R.V., Jeremiah G., Webb W.A. and Wheeler M. Detection of anabolic steroid administration to athletes. J. Ster. Biochem. 11, 913-917, 1979.
6. Murthy L.R., Johnson M.P., Rowley D.R., Young C.Y.F., Scario P.T. and Tindall D.J. Characterization of steroid receptors in human prostate using Mibolerone. The Prostate 8, 241-253, 1986.

Potential of HPLC for screening and confirmation of diuretics

Rosa Ventura, Jordi Segura and Rafael de la Torre

Department of Pharmacology and Toxicology, Municipal Institute
for Medical Research, Passeig Maritim 25-29, 08003 Barcelona
Spain

Abstract - The diuretics and those substances which inhibit
renal excretion of other drugs (i.e. probenecid) have been
recently added to the list of banned substances in sport (IOC
Medical Commission). New methodologies for the detection of
such substances in urine are being proposed. Taking into
account physico-chemical and metabolic factors, a fast and
comprehensive screening methodology is being proposed. Urines
are extracted (ethyl acetate) in alkaline medium (pH=9).
Under these conditions, the basic, neutral and weak acid
diuretics are satisfactorily extracted. The yield for strong
acids is low but enough to generally detect their ingestion.
HPLC analysis is carried out by reverse phase chromatography
by using gradient elution (0.05 M ammonium acetate pH=5,
acetonitrile) and UV detection (270 nm). The presence of
strong acid diuretics can subsequently be confirmed by ether
extraction of the previous aqueous phase after acidification.
The ingestion of most of the diuretics included in the IOC
list may be evidenced with the described methodology. In
addition, the chromatographic conditions used, are compatible
with confirmation by HPLC-MS.

INTRODUCTION

The diuretics and those substances which inhibit renal excretion of other
drugs (i.e. probenecid) have been recently added to the list of banned substances in sports (International Olympic Committee, IOC Medical Commission).
Such substances were controlled for the 1988 Summer and Winter Olympic Games.

The substances have been used illicitly in sport competitions to reduce body
weight in order to be qualified for another weight category (i.e. weight-
lifting). Often they are used to reduce the urinary concentration of other
banned substances to levels below the detection limits of analytical
techniques routinely used in doping control. In the latter case, such effect
can be accomplished by an increase of urinary flow or by an inhibition of the
excretion of drugs.

The introduction of diuretics into the routines for doping control requires
the development of analytical procedures which are able to detect the largest
number of substances using a minimum of different screening procedures.

Depending on their acid/base behavior (pKa), diuretics included in the lists
of IOC can be classified into four groups: basics, neutrals, weak acids and
strong acids (Table 1). The great diversity on chemical structures and
physico-chemical properties of substances belonging to this group, make it
difficult to develop assays using common screening techniques. Screening
procedures described until now (ref. 1,2,3) are designed specifically to
detect some groups of diuretics, but not in a comprehensive approach. Tisdall
et al. (ref. 1) described an HPLC technique using two mobile phases for the
detection of thiazide diuretics. De Croo et al. (ref. 2) proposed an HPLC
technique also with two mobile phases for the detection of weak acid diuretics and strong acid, basic and neutral diuretics. Fullinfaw et al. (ref. 3)
have described recently an HPLC procedure for the detection of acid diuretics

TABLE 1. Classification of diuretics depending on physico-chemical properties

	compound	pKa	log P
BASIC DIURETICS:	triamterene	6.2	0.98
	amiloride	8.7	
NEUTRAL DIURETICS:	spironolactone		2.78
	canrenone		2.68
WEAK ACID DIURETICS:	benzthiazide		1.46
	bendroflumethiazide	8.5	1.19
	diclofenamide	7.4-8.6	1.03
	hydroclorothiazide	7.0-9.2	-0.07
	acetazolamide	7.2-9.0 (25°C)	-0.26
	chlorthalidone	9.4	
STRONG ACID DIURETICS:	bumetanide	5.2	0.12
	ethacrynic acid	3.5	-0.81
	furosemide	3.9	-0.83

after an acid extraction of the samples. Our strategy for the analysis of diuretics (basic, neutral, weak acid and strong acid), involves a single HPLC technique which is compatible both with UV detection and interfacing to a mass spectrometer. The extraction procedure of urine samples has been designed for the simultaneous recovery of most of diuretics.

EXPERIMENTAL

Extraction of urine samples
Urine samples (5 ml) were made alkaline (pH 9-10) with sodium hydroxide and 1 g of sodium chloride was added. Samples were extracted with 6 ml of ethyl acetate. After centrifugation, the organic phase was separated and taken to dryness under nitrogen stream at 40°C. After reconstitution with mobile phase, the extracts (basic fraction) were directly analyzed by high-performance liquid chromatography (HPLC). For the detection of strong acid diuretics, the aqueous phase remaining from the previous extraction was acidified with 40% phosphoric acid (pH 2-2.5) and extracted with 6 ml of diethylether. After centrifugation the organic phase was separated and extracted with 5 ml of phosphate buffer 0.2 M pH 2.5. After centrifugation the organic phase was separated and taken to dryness under nitrogen stream at 40°C. After reconstitution with mobile phase, the extracts (acid fraction) were directly analyzed under the same chromatographic conditions as described above for the basic extract.

High-performance liquid chromatography
Separation was carried out using 5-μm reversed phase columns (Ultrasphere ODS 25 x 0.4 cm; Beckman, USA) fitted to a Series 400 solvent delivery system, an ISS-100 automatic injector and a LC235 diode array UV detector adjusted to 270 nm (all from Perkin Elmer Corp., USA).

The mobile phase was an ammonium acetate buffer 0.05 M pH 5 (adjusted with acetic acid) and acetonitrile using gradient elution (see fig 1). The flow rate was 1 ml min^{-1}. Ammonium phosphate buffer (pH 3) was also used, instead of acetate buffer, during the development of the methodology.

Application to excretion studies
24 Hour urine samples were obtained from healthy male volunteers following ingestion of the diuretics (furosemide, hydrochlorothiazide, spironolactone, amiloride, triamterene, bumetanide).

RESULTS

The recoveries obtained for diuretics added to urine samples and extracted using the described procedure are summarized in Table 2. The effect of the HPLC mobile phase composition on the retention times of the different classes of diuretics was also studied. The effects of the acetonitrile percentage and ammonium buffer are shown in fig 2 and fig 3 respectively.

TABLE 2.   Compounds recovered in acid and basic extracts

basic extract	acid extract
amiloride hydrochlorothiazide triamterene furosemide benzthiazide bendroflumethiazide bumetanide spironolactone	furosemide bumetanide
recoveries ranged from 38 to 93%	recoveries ranged from 70 to 80%

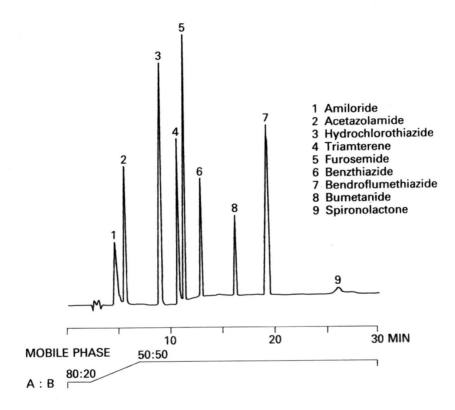

1 Amiloride
2 Acetazolamide
3 Hydrochlorothiazide
4 Triamterene
5 Furosemide
6 Benzthiazide
7 Bendroflumethiazide
8 Bumetanide
9 Spironolactone

Fig 1.   Chromatogram of a methanolic standard solution. Mobile phase: A.
0.05 M ammonium acetate buffer pH 5; B. acetonitrile.

Chromatograms of basic extracts of urine samples obtained after the ingestion
of amiloride and hydrochlorothiazide are shown in fig 4.

Chromatograms of acid and basic extracts of urine samples after the ingestion
of triamterene and furosemide are shown in fig 5. To illustrate the compatibility of the present HPLC methodology with mass spectrometry (HPLC-MS
thermospray interface), the mass spectra of a pure standard and that obtained
after an excretion study of amiloride are shown in fig 6.

DISCUSSION

The extraction recoveries of diuretics from spiked urine samples demonstrated
that all of the drugs (see Table 2) can be extracted in the basic fraction
with a yield high enough to allow their detection. In the case of the basic
diuretics, their extraction at an alkaline pH is favored because of the pKa;
for neutral diuretics extraction is due to the high partition coefficient

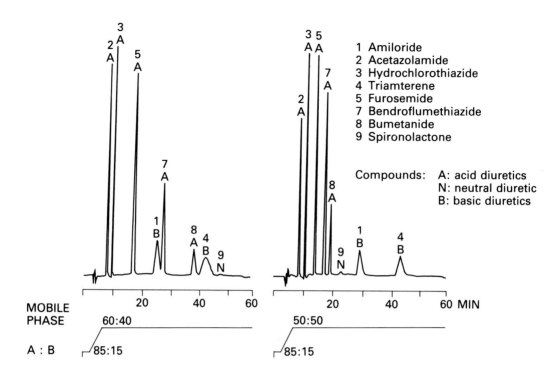

Fig 2.   Effect of acetonitrile proportion on the chromatographic separation
of a methanolic mixture of diuretics. Mobile phase: A. water pH 3
(phosphoric acid); B. acetonitrile.

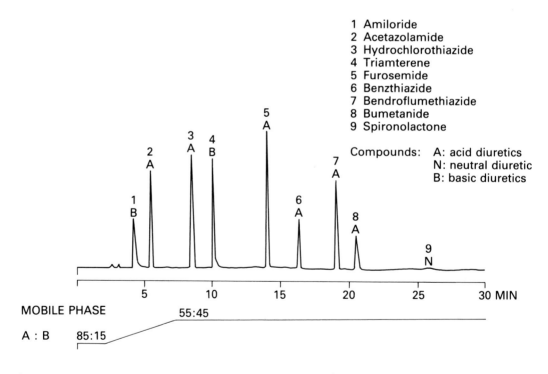

Fig 3.   Effect of ammonium salt buffer on the chromatographic separation of a
methanolic mixture of diuretics. Mobile phase: A. 0.05 M ammonium
phosphate buffer pH 3 (phosphoric acid); B. acetonitrile.

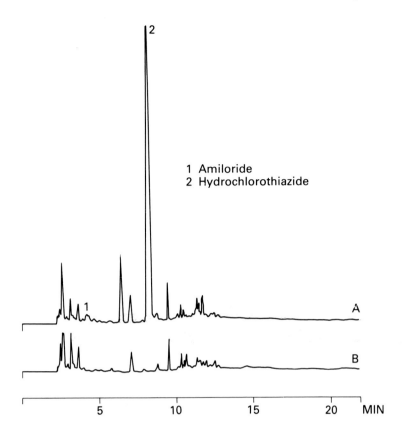

Fig 4. Chromatograms of basic extracts: A. urine collected from 0 to 24 h after amiloride and hydrochlorothiazide intake (5 and 50 mg, respectively); B. blank urine sample.

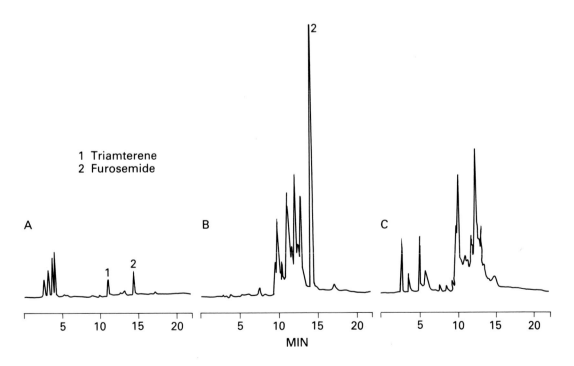

Fig 5. Chromatograms of: A. basic extract of a urine sample collected after triamterene and furosemide intake; B. acid extract of the same urine sample; C. acid extract of a blank urine sample.

A

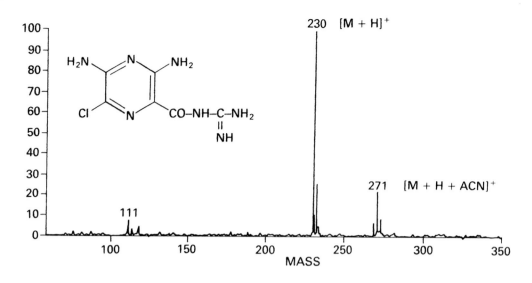

B

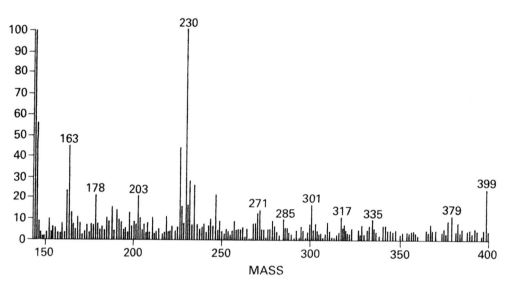

Fig 6.   Thermospray mass spectrum of amiloride (mw 229): A. mass spectrum
          from a methanolic standard solution; B. mass spectrum from a basic
          extract of a urine collected after amiloride intake.

(see Table 1), and for weak acid diuretics the pKa, although lower, is
sufficiently close to the extraction pH to allow its recovery in the basic extract. An
additional factor which facilitates the detection of diuretics in the basic fraction is
that the extract is cleaner with fewer interfering substances as compared with the acid
extract (see figs 4 and 5). The salting out effect used in the basic extraction improves
the recovery of strong acid diuretics. The use of ethyl acetate as extracting solvent rather
than diethylether (ref 4) improves the whole extraction procedure. As seen in figure 2,
small changes in the concentration of acetonitrile in the mobile phase gives rise to important
alterations on the retention time of acid and neutral diuretics. When an ammonium buffer
is used instead of water, the retention time of basic diuretics is altered and the time
of analysis is shortened. Ion pairing reagents, which are not always compatible with HPLC-
MS, were not required. An ammonium phosphate buffer has been used with good performance
during the development of the methodology, but in order to facilitate the compatibility
of the chromatograhic system with some commonly used interfaces (thermospray) when coupling
HPLC to MS, a more volatile ammonium acetate buffer was chosen.

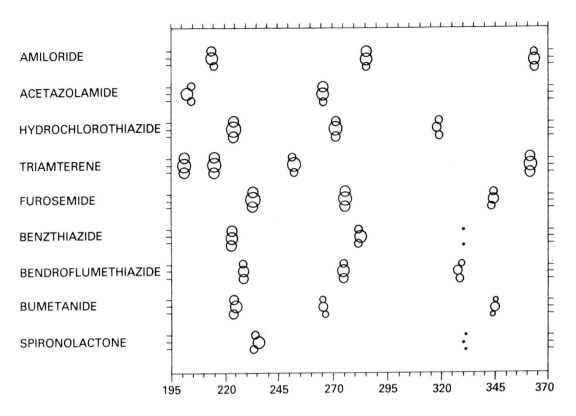

Fig 7. Absorbance profile map of some diuretics. Diode array detector.

The working UV wavelength of 270 nm was selected for the detection of diuretics. Other wavelengths can provide useful information when using diode
array detectors (see fig 7). Some diuretics, such as spironolactone, have a
maximum absorption at 235 nm, nevertheless the extensive hepatic metabolism
of such a drug make it unnecessary to choose a wavelength other than 270 nm,
since some of the major metabolites (like canrenone) have a maximum absorption near 270 nm.

The coupling experiment between HPLC and MS using a thermospray interface is
quite illustrative of the compatibility of the chromatographic system.
Results obtained using a plasmaspray interface are also promising, considering the high sensitivity and the less stringent requirements for the composition of the mobile phase (data not shown). Regardless of the choice of
interface, in the future the HPLC-MS coupling approach may become the
technique of choice for the detection and confirmation of such compounds in
doping control.

REFERENCES

1. P.A. Tisdall, T.P. Moyer and J.P. Anhalt, Clin. Chem. 26/6, 702-706 (1980).
2. F.De Croo, W. Van Den Bossche and P. De Moerloose, J. Chromatogr. 325,
    395-411 (1985).
3. R.O. Fullinfaw, R.W. Bury and R.F.W. Moulds, J. Chromatogr. 415, 345-356
    (1987).
4. W. Schänzer,   5th Workshop on Dope Analysis, Cologne 1987.

ACKNOWLEDGEMENT

The authors thank Dr. Daniel Fraise (Lab. Spectrométrie de Masse, SCA, CNRS,
Vernaison, France) for his cooperation in the HPLC-MS analyses.

Identification of drug metabolites by gas chromatography – mass spectrometry

Slobodan Rendić

Department of Pharmaceutical Chemistry, Faculty of Pharmacy and
Biochemistry, University of Zagreb,
41000 Zagreb, Yugoslavia

Abstract - In the last ten years a variety of instrumental methods using
mass spectrometry have been developed, to determine drugs and their
metabolites in biological sample. Applications of the GC/MS/COMP system in
qualitative and quantitative determinations of different classes of drugs
and metabolites has spread primarily to biochemistry, medicine and toxicology in addition to control the use of doping agents in sport. The methods
of sample preparation and derivatization reagents used are suitable for
GC/MS analysis of parent drugs and metabolites with respect to volatility,
thermal stability and fragmentation pattern. As examples determinations of
metabolites in urine samples after administration of mefenorex, I, etafedrine, V and drug labelled MUCAINE[R] are presented. In addition, influence
of different factors, particularly those inhibiting metabolism of doping
agents are discussed.

FACTORS INFLUENCING DRUG'S METABOLIC PATTERN

In doping control, identification of metabolites in a sample contributes to the evidence for a
drug having passed through the body of an examinee. Positive identification of metabolites is
however not exclusively dependent on the skill of laboratory personal, but also on other
circumstances varying from case to case. Furthermore, metabolic pathways of the particular
drug, and consequently the metabolites actualy present in a biological sample, may be
influenced by number of factors, such as inhibition and induction of drug metabolism by other
drugs (administered concomitantly), and physiological factors, such as age, sex, hormone
imbalance, diet and others, have to be considered for a valid interpretation of the results.
Attention should be paied to the extent of inhibition of the enzymes belonging to the group
of monooxygenases dependent on cytochrome P-450. These enzymes catalyse oxidative and redu-
ctive metabolic reactions of many of drugs and the latter's metabolic profiles can vary. On
the other hand, elevated blood levels and prolonged half-lives of the parent drug have been
observed and drug's $t_{1/2}$ will influence the pattern of metabolites at sampling time (ref.1).
In addition to other drugs known as potent inhibitors of these enzymes, the anabolic hormone
stanozolol has been found to act as a strong inhibitor of cytochrome P-450 dependent monooxygenases. The inhibitory action of stanozolol has been attributed to the nitrogen atom of
the pirazole ring, a high-affinity ligand complexing with cytochrome P-450 (ref. 2). Its
influence on in vitro metabolism of other drugs is under study in our laboratory. For
illustration the banned drugs which elimination is impaired by H_2-receptor antagonist cimetidine are listed in Table 1.

Table 1. The banned drugs which elimination is impaired with cimetidine
(ref. 3).

Drug	Effect/Mechanism
Beta-blockers propranolol labetalol metoprolol	Blood concentration elevated/decreased metabolism
morphine	Prolonged response to drug/decreased hepatic blood flow
caffeine	Blood concentration elevated/decreased metabolism

GC/MS IN IDENTIFICATION OF METABOLITES

The goal of the GC/MS method is to structurally determine both the parent compound and its metabolites in the same sample, using essentially the same procedure. The procedure for determination of drugs and metabolites in biological samples is presented in Scheme 1.

SCHEME 1. Procedure for determination of drugs and metabolites by GC/MS.

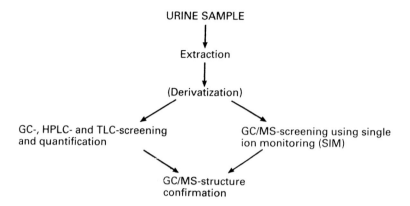

Using the extraction procedures recommended by the IOC Medical Commission (Scheme 2,ref.4), drugs and metabolites are separated already at the begining of the analysis according to their physico-chemical properties, and according to the form of urinary excretion (free drugs are separated from conjugates).

Although many drugs and metabolites can be analysed by GS/MS directly in organic extracts without additional evaporation and derivatization, drugs possessing very polar functional groups in the molecule have to be derivatized before the analysis. After derivatization chemical and structural properties are modified in a such a way as to produce more stable and more volatile derivatives, and the most abundant ions in mass spectra are obtained at higher m/e values. By combining different derivatization reagents to act on the same sample,

SCHEME 2. Extraction procedures used for analysis of drugs and metabolites.

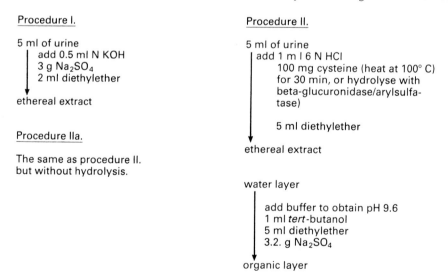

additional information on the structure could be obtained. In our laboratory, in addition to the derivatization with trifluoroacetic acid anhydride (TFAA), the method of "selective derivatization" introduced by Donike et al. (5,6) is used. The latter procedure is also used when polyhydroxylated compounds are present in the sample, TMSO-derivatives of which are more stable.

The following examples will illustrate structure determinations of metabolites using the methods discussed.

SCHEME 3. Fragmentation pattern of mefenorex, I and metabolites.

Mefenorex I

Amphetamine, II

IV

III

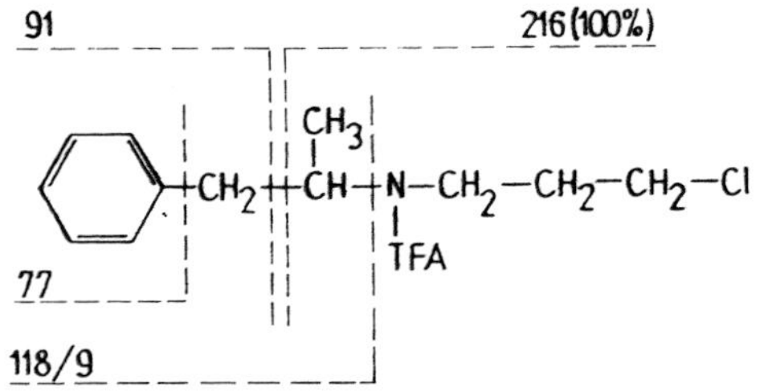

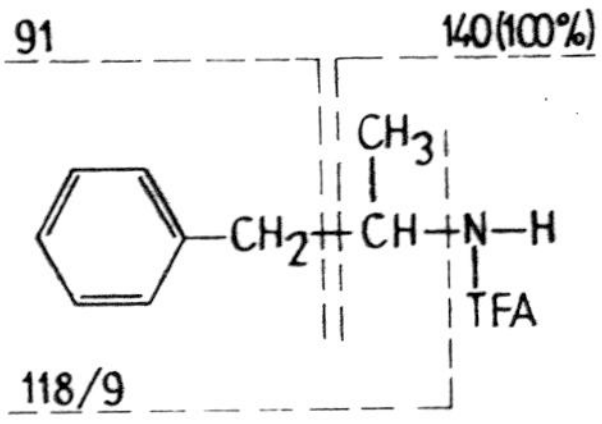

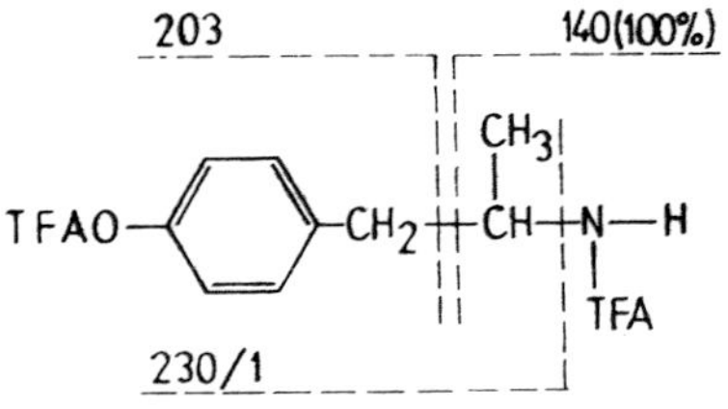

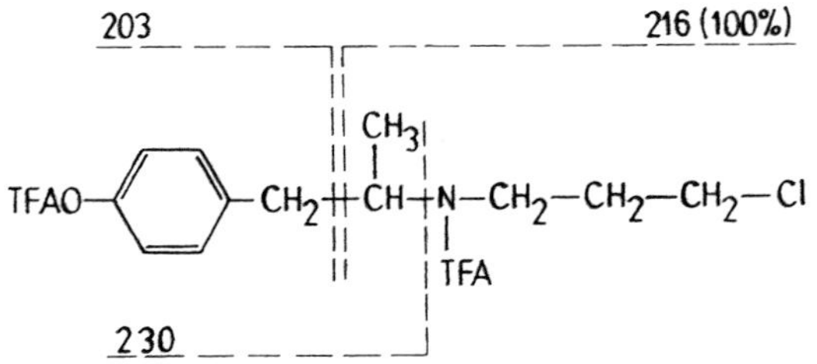

SCHEME 4. Fragmentation pattern of etafedrine, V and metabolites.

Etafedrine, V

Ephedrine, VII
(metabolite)

Metabolite, VI

Norephedrine, VIII
(metabolite)

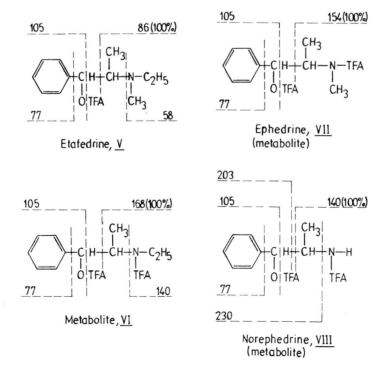

After p.o. administration of the stimulant drugs mefenorex, I and etafedrine, V , both compounds are extensively metabolized (Scheme 3 and 4, respectively) by oxidative N-dealkylation, hydroxylation of the aromatic ring, and of the C-atom adjacent to the aromatic ring. The metabolites thus produced are amphetamine, II and hydroxylated compounds III and IV (resulting from mefenorex, I), and ephedrine, VII , norephedrine, VIII and N-demethylated compound VI (resulting from etafedrine, V). As presented in Scheme 3 and 4, the most abundant ions after derivatization with TFAA are used for the structure determination of metabolites (i.e. ions at m/e 216, 168, 154 and 140), in addition to the less abundant ions at m/e 230, 203, 118 and 105.

Fragments which are used for determination of compounds possessing similar structure after "selective derivatization" are presented in Scheme 5.

A practical approach of using the derivatization methods described, in determinations of drug metabolites in real samples will be illustrated by the following example. In the urine of athlete taking drug MUCAINE[R], which was allowed to be used by contestants, metabolites of mephentermine, IX (compounds XI and XII) were identified (Scheme 5). The preparation labelled MUCAINE[R] contains, in addition to the drug – the local anesthetic oxethazaine – the hydroxydes of aluminium and magnesium. As shown in Scheme 6, oxethazaine possesses a mephentermine-like structure. It was concluded, therefore, that the metabolites might originate from mephentermine which is, in turn, produced either by metabolic or chemical degradation of oxethazaine (Scheme 6).

SCHEME 5 . Structures of mephentermine, IX and metabolites identified
after administration of MUCAINE[R].

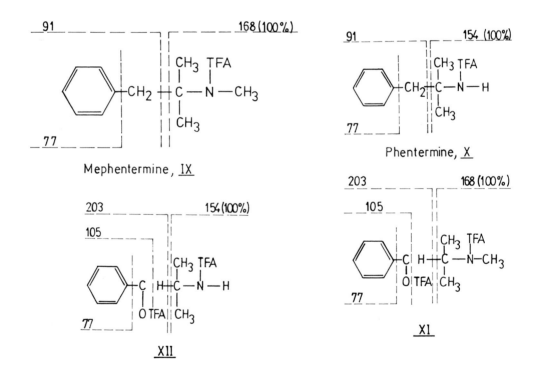

When MUCAINE[R] was extracted low concentrations of mephentermine were identified in the extract   of the drug indicating that mephentermine was produced by chemical degradation of oxethazaine. The mephentermine already present in the preparation, is following an intake, further metabolised to metabolites XI and XII . The structure of these metabolites was similar to the metabolites of etafedrine as shown by their mass spectra (Scheme 4).

SCHEME **6.** Structure of oxethazaine.

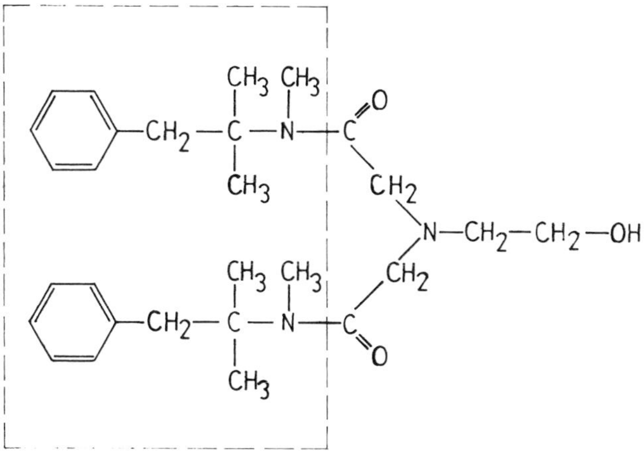

Similarly, drugs belonging to other groups of doping agents are excreted unchanged (as the

SCHEME **7.** Metabolic pathways of propranolol.

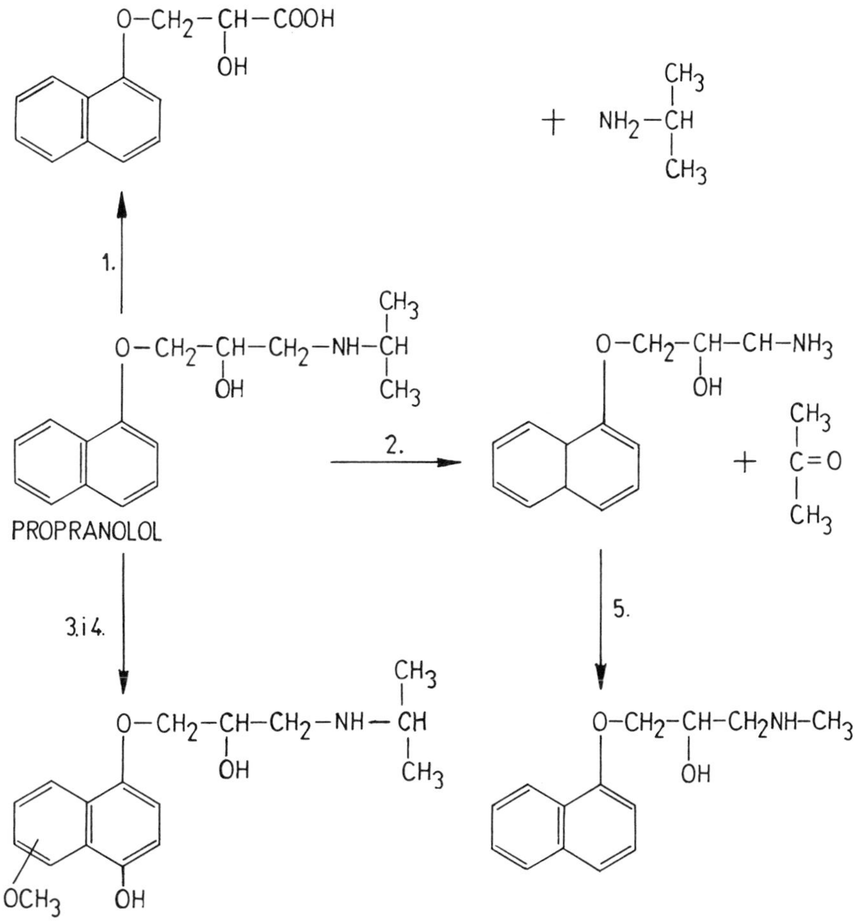

Reactions:

1. Oxidative deamination
2. Oxidative dealkylation
3. Hydroxylation of aromatic rings
4. O-methylation
5. N-methylation

Enzymes involved:

Cytochrome P-450 dependent microsomal monooxygenases

O-methyl transferase
N-methyl transferase

most of diuretics) or are more or less extensively metabolised, depending on their physico-chemical properties. For illustration, the metabolic pattern of propranolol is presented in Scheme 7, showing that several structurally different metabolites are formed. In addition to the parent compound, metabolites produced by reactions assignated as 3 and 4 are most often found in the urine samples.

REFERENCES

1. H.A. Griem, in Concepts in Drug Metabolism (Eds. P. Jenner and B.Testa), pp. 219-263, Marcel Dekker Inc., New York (1981).
2. S.Rendić and H.H. Ruf, Biochem. Pharamacol., 37, 766-768 (1988).
3. M.Nazario, Drug Intell. Clin. Pharm., 20, 342-348 (1986).
4. M.Donike, K.R.Bärwald, V.Christ, G.Opferman, G.Sigmund, J.Zimmerman and W.Schänzer, in Sports Medicine in Track and Field Athletics (Eds. A. Ljungqvist, P.Peltokallio and H.Tikkanen), pp. 117-130, Lehtikanta Oy, Kouvola (1985).
5. M.Donike, J.Chromatogr., 103, 91-112 (1975).
6. M.Donike and J.Derenbach, Z.Anal. Chem., 279, 128-131 (1976).

Mass spectrometry instrumentation in the 1990's

James R. Shipe, Jr.

Department of Pathology, University of Virginia Medical Center, Charlottesville, Virginia, USA

Abstract - The combined techniques of gas chromatography/mass spectrometry (GC/MS) have been used for the analysis of endogenous steroid profiles in biological materials for more than 20 years. The high resolving power of capillary column GC/MS has been applied to the screening methods for detection of synthetic anabolic steroids for over a decade. Most of the improvements in recent years have been in computerized instrument control and data acquisition with relatively few significant changes in mass spectrometer hardware itself. Recent advances in both sample preparation and mass spectrometry instrumentation will undoubtedly figure prominently in the field of doping control. Now commercially available, laboratory robotics for automating sample preparation offer significant benefits. Emerging technologies such as tandem mass spectrometry (GC/MS/MS), when combined with novel ionization and sample introduction, provide significant advantages over the instrumentation in widespread use today.

INTRODUCTION

In the field of drug testing, the detection of doping with synthetic anabolic steroids represents a challenging analytical problem due in part to the complexity of normal steroid profile and the large number of banned anabolics and metabolites which must be detected. Since the initial radioimmunoassay screening procedures were replaced by GC/MS, the fundamental analysis has actually changed very little. The lengthy and tedious sample extraction, is followed by a long capillary gas chromatographic separation. The GC/MS itself generates a large amount of data for each sample and requires a highly specialized individual to interpret the data. The evolution of the analysis to its present form has been marked by significant refinements in sample preparation, gas chromatographic separation and data handling capabilities.

The mass spectrometric portion of the screening analysis, however, represents a mature technology. The usual procedure, in which selected ion monitoring (SIM) of a few characteristic ions formed in electron impact (EI) ionization, has changed very little. Recent reports of anabolic steroid analysis with new state-of-the-art equipment, both commercially available and under development in research laboratories, hold great promise for the field of doping control. I will mention some of the more interesting techniques and discuss their benefits and limitations for doping control laboratories.

SAMPLE PREPARATION

The discussion of initial steps involving the extraction of the anabolic steroids from the urine specimen may appear far afield from a discussion of mass spectrometry instrumentation. In fact, the sophistication of these early steps often determines the degree of selectivity achieved by the second step, the actual screening and confirmation by GC/MS. Conversely, the greater the specificity and selectivity of the MS step, the less stringent are the requirements of the sample cleanup. Another indication for consideration of this topic here is the logical combination of these two steps on the same instrument, analogous to the interfacing of an autosampler to a benchtop GC/MS.

Historically, liquid-liquid extraction was usually combined with one or more with liquid-solid extractions using mini-columns containing XAD-2 or Extrelut. Solid phase extraction (SPE) using C_{18} or silica columns was found to give cleaner chromatograms, higher recoveries and is the most commonly used today. The latest generation of bonded phase columns (eg. Bond Elut Certify) combine strong cation exchange and C_{18} reversed phase which allow retention by both ionic and the usual reversed phase mechanisms. For the extraction of drugs of abuse, these columns provide both high recovery and exceptionally clean extracts. Their application to the extraction of urinary anabolic steroids has not been reported, however preliminary experiments in our laboratory indicate they are superior to conventional SPE columns.

In the future, one of the most powerful tools for the purification of anabolic steroids from biological materials may be immunoaffinity chromatography (IAC) where selective retention is based on antibody-antigen interaction. Recent reports (Ref. 1) demonstrate this to be a most promising technique for specific isolation of steroids on a column containing immobilized antibodies to these steroids. A reusable column containing a mixture of antibodies would allow many analytes to be separated and analyzed on-line.

Laboratory automation systems, now in routine use, can completely automate the extraction of steroids by the same techniques used manually in doping control laboratories. These systems, such as the one produced by Zymark, automate all the steps starting with a raw urine sample and finishing with a derivatized extract loaded into a GC autosampler vial and ready for analysis by GC/MS. Robotics is expected to play an important role in the analysis of steroids by directly interfacing sample preparation to the subsequent analytical step.

GAS CHROMATOGRAPHY-MASS SPECTROMETRY

Most modern mass spectrometers which have gas chromatographs equipped with fused silica capillary columns are suitable for the qualitative analysis of urinary anabolic steroids and metabolites. Our first experience with GC/MS for anabolic screening made use of a double-focusing high resolution magnetic sector instrument operated at nominal mass resolution. The quality of the ion optics allowed high sensitivity analyses even when acquiring full scan spectra, however the high initial cost of the system and complexity of operation have limited the widespread use of sector instruments. The most popular instruments today are the bench-top GC/MS systems which are compact and relatively easy to operate. With their low cost quadrupole analyzers, these bench-top instruments allow most laboratories access to GC/MS although at a reduced level of performance. The Hewlett-Packard recently introduced a PC-controlled Mass Selective Detector (MSD). The MSD, widely used in drug analysis laboratories, provides an electron impact (EI) quadrupole mass analyzer complete with gas chromatograph and data system for less than $50,000. The instrument control and data processing is automatically controlled using a multitasking data system based on industry standard 80386-based personal computers. Because of the low detection limits required for the analysis of anabolic steroids, the EI data is generally acquired in the selected ion monitoring (SIM) mode, where only a few ions for each drug are monitored at selected times during the chromatographic run. At very low sample concentrations the relative intensities of some of the selected ions are often obscured by the chemical background and confirmation using full scan EI spectra is not possible. The low cost and ease of use of the MSD however, will continue to make the MSD an established fixture in many laboratories.

Another technology which may evolve to prominence in the 1990s is GC/MS analysis using the Ion Trap Detector (ITD) from Finnigan MAT. A recent review article (Ref. 2) discusses ion trap technology in some detail. As a mass analyzer, all ions produced are stored in the ITD and selectively ejected into the electron multiplier by ramping the amplitude of the rf voltage, thus generating a conventional EI spectrum. The long residence time of the ions formed inside the mass analyzer enables full scan spectra at the picogram level. In fact, in contrast to quadrupole-based instruments, the acquisition technique of SIM in the ion trap adds little to the overall sensitivity of the analysis. This availability of the full scan mass spectrum is essential for the unambiguous confirmation of the presence of anabolic steroids. One unique problem with the ITD is "space charging" which is seen in high sample concentration, background from the sample or severe column bleed. The large number of ions interact, influencing the charge of their neighbors, to produce spectra more closely resembling that obtained using chemical ionization (CI). The addition of automatic gain control (AGC) to second generation instruments minimized this effect by automatically decreasing the ionization time whenever excessive numbers of ions are being formed.

The use of AGC algorithms to reduce ion populations did improve the dynamic range of the ITD, however there remained instabilities in measuring ion isotopic abundances because AGC could not compensate for self-CI which occurs with neutral species (ref. 3). Using deuterated analogs for quantitative drug analysis is now routine in most laboratories, yet few if any publications have reported its successful application using the IDT, confirming our experience of considerable imprecision in the measurement of the ratios of the selected analyte ion and its deuterated analog in stable isotope dilution GC/MS. Most published methods use homologs or stable isotope analogs which can be resolved chromatographically. The latest generation of ion trap instrument has additional electronics and software which have made substantial improvements in the data acquisition portion of the scan function. This addition of an axial modulation (ac voltage signal) to the end caps of the ion trap has been reported to both increase sensitivity and improve resolution over the original RF-only scan function. It is obvious that ion trap technology is rapidly evolving and may, in the future, offer significant advantages over quadrupole analyzers in both initial cost, sensitivity and mass analysis modes. While the processing power of the personal computers used in these systems lags behind the rest of the computer industry, they allow one to use relatively inexpensive industry standard peripherals such as hard drives, removable tape cartridges and CD-ROM's.

TANDEM MASS SPECTROMETRY (MS/MS)

MS/MS is one of the mass analysis modes which may offer considerable benefits over conventional MS for many analytical problems. Tandem mass spectrometry, as recently reviewed by Bush (ref. 4), is not a new technique and the instrumentation which has been used is quite diverse. Commercially produced MS/MS systems of this decade have been primarily designed around triple quadrupole mass analyzers, in which two mass filters are joined by means of a rf-only collision chamber. Ions produced in the source can be selected by the first analyzer (Q1) and the selected "parent" ions collided with neutral gas molecules in the collision chamber (Q2) to produce "daughter" ions. These fragment ions, produced by collisionally induced dissociation (CID), can be scanned by the third quadrupole (Q3) to produce daughter ion spectra thus providing a highly specific means of identifying compounds in complex mixtures. Quantitative analysis is most commonly performed by a technique referred to as selected reaction monitoring (SRM) in which only the most intense daughter ion from each parent is monitored with the third quadrupole. With appropriate choice derivatives and ions selected for parent-to-daughter transitions, improvements in specificity are almost always achieved are often quite dramatic.

The measurement of urinary testosterone-epitestoserone (T/E) ratios using MS/MS is one preliminary application we have investigated (ref.5). The usual measurement of T/E ratios using multiple ion monitoring GC/MS is complicated by both their normally low concentration and the presence of closely eluting endogenous steroids which are present in far greater concentration. Figure 1 illustrates the selectivity obtained using selected reaction monitoring of a urine extract derivatized to form the very stable methoxime, t-butyldimethylsilyl (t-BDMS) ether derivatives. The advantage of t-BDMS derivatives for MS/MS is that they generally give rise to intense molecular ions (Fig 2). CID of these parents produce daughter ion spectra having M - 57 as their base peak, corresponding to the loss of the C_4H_9 radical. For testosterone and epitestosterone, analysis in the selected reaction monitoring mode detected the parent-to-daughter transitions (m/z 431-m/z 374) and the corresponding transitions for the deuterated internal standard d_2-testosterone (m/z 433-m/z 376).

From these preliminary studies we conclude that rapid, sensitive and selective quantitation is possible with MS/MS on short fused silica columns. The selective screening for larger numbers of compounds may be achieved using longer columns and specific parent-to-daughter transitions monitored in selected time windows during the chromatographic separation. It has also been recommended that the technique be used for confirmation of drugs present in such low concentrations that the relative intensities from full scan spectral data are made unintrepretable because of the high background chemical noise .

The detection limits achieved using MS/MS are comparable to that of single stage MS in spite of considerable transmission loss (90-95%) of ion intensity always observed with tandem quadrupole analyzers. MS/MS instruments, which have been carefully optimized for maximum ion transmission, achieve sensitivity because much of the chemical noise is filtered out in Q1 and the signal can be increased to an even greater degree by simply increasing the electron multiplier voltage. The best sensitivity using SRM is obtained, as in the previous example, when one chooses a parent ion which carries most of the ion current from a selected analyte and produces only a few intense daughter ions. While the use of soft ionization techniques and choice of derivatization used can help improve detection limits for some compounds, improved sensitivity using MS/MS is not guaranteed. In tandem instruments, the ion source, mass filters and collision cell are physically separated and significant losses in ion intensity occur during each stage of transmission.

The problems associated with sensitivity loss during ion transmission may be improved in the future by the recent developments in ion-trapping techniques where the different stages of MS/MS are separated in time rather than space. Two such technologies, the ion trap mass spectrometer (ITMS) and Fourier transform-ion cyclotron resonance spectrometer (FT-ICR), are promising candidates for providing high sensitivity MS/MS with the added possibility of simplicity and low cost.

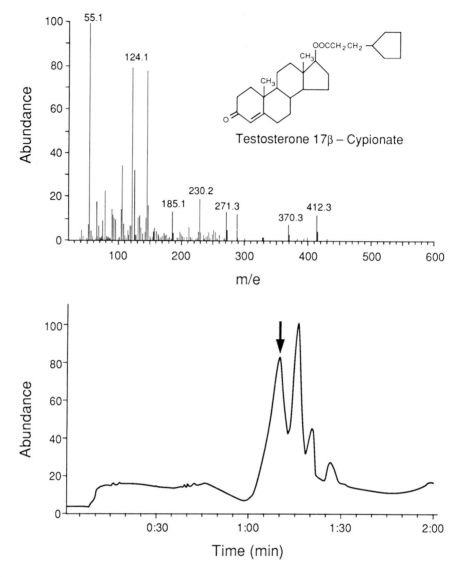

Fig. 1. Selected reaction monitoring of urinary T/E ratio

MS/MS WITH ION-TRAPPING INSTRUMENTS

FT-ICR instruments trap ions with high efficiency by means of both electric and magnetic fields. This ability to trap daughter ions with good efficiency has several advantages for MS/MS experiments such as the possibility of multiple stages (parent-to-daughter-to-granddaughter). Another exciting feature, unique to FT-ICR spectrometers, is the ability to provide high resolution mass measurements which greatly adds to the selectivity of daughter ion analysis in selected reaction monitoring MS/MS.

In spite of these impressive features, FT-ICR mass spectrometers have several limitations which must be overcome in the future before it can become a wide spread in analytical laboratories. The low operating pressure required (typically 10^{-8} Torr) by the ICR cell has created many problems for both interfacing instruments to a gas chromatograph and the production of daughter ions by collision with a relatively high pressure pulse of gas. These problems are now being addressed in a number of research laboratories and the prototype systems for sample introduction (external ion sources , 2-section cells) and low pressure ionization (photodissociation, electron induced dissociation) have demonstrated that these problems can be overcome. The second limitation, which may limit the greater availability of these instruments for real world use, is the cost and size of the superconducting magnets used in these systems.

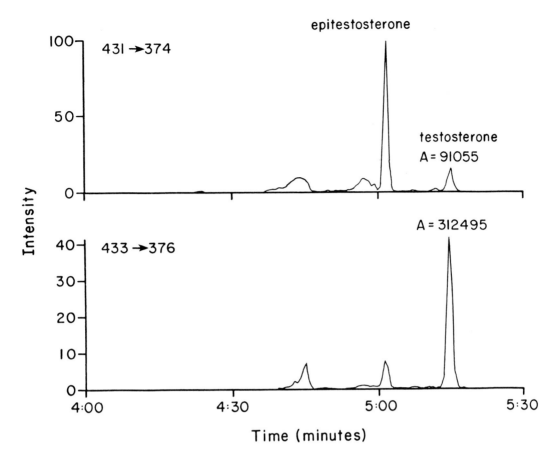

Fig. 2. Electron impact mass spectrum of methoxime, t-butyldimethylsilyl ether derivative of testosterone

MS/MS using the ion trap technology mentioned earlier may represent the first low cost bench top instrument to gain widespread use. As in FT-ICR ,the stages of analysis in ITMS are similar in that they are tandem in time: ionization, stabilization of a single parent ion, collision with inert gas, and detection of daughter ions occur sequentially using complex scan functions. In contrast, the ITMS analyzer actually requires a high (10^{-3} Torr) pressure of a background gas such as helium to dampen the trajectories of the ions and increase trapping efficiency. Aside from more sophisticated instrument control software, very little additional hardware is added to the standard ion trap detector in order to perform MS/MS experiments. In light of this, the high cost of the instruments now commercially available is difficult to justify and can be expected to fall in the very near future. As a very selective detector for a GC, such a system could have several advantages over the triple quadrupole MS/MS systems in terms of automation, sensitivity, ease of use and initial cost.

In all of the instruments mentioned above, directly interfaced high resolution fused silica capillary GC columns have traditionally provided the best performance in terms of sensitivity and selectivity. For the analysis of a large number of drugs in doping control, even the expensive and sophisticated technique of GC/MS/MS still necessitates sample extraction and derivatization. Whereas screening by selected ion monitoring GC/MS generally requires at least partial chromatographic resolution of analyte ions from background ion intensities, in GC/MS/MS coeluting endogenous peaks are not a concern. Short sections of fused silica capillary therefore provide sufficient chromatographic separation and represent a convenient, easily automated means of sample introduction.

ALTERNATIVE SAMPLE INTRODUCTION

From its inception MS/MS was recognized as a useful tool for analysis of target compounds in complex mixtures. The early work held promise that sample extraction and chromatographic separation could be done away with entirely. One such study, based on dissociation of metastable ions of steroids in magnetic sector (BE) instruments, indicated the ability to individually quantitate three estrogens in a synthetic mixture as they distilled from a direct insertion probe (Ref. 6). A decade later, one of the first generation of triple stage quadrupoles was used to demonstrate the utility of MS/MS for screening of drugs and metabolites in plasma applied directly to a heated solids probe sample inlet (Ref. 7). However, the high background caused by thermal decomposition of the sample matrix, generally prevented detection in the ng/ml range and thus limited its usefulness as a routine analytical technique. Another practical limitation of direct sample introduction for screening purposes is that drugs of similar structure, such as the anabolic steroids, vaporize from the probe virtually simultaneously thus limiting the number of parent-to-daughter transitions which can be sequenced.

Nonetheless the direct exposure probe (DEP) is frequently useful in the drug identification of samples which would be difficult using conventional techniques. Many thermally labile samples can be vaporized without decomposition by application directly to a current-programmed rhenium wire filament. As an example, the analysis of black market injectable steroid preparations is complicated by both the oil based vehicle and the fact many are in the form of esters (decanoate, cypionate, enanthate, etc.). For these compounds extraction from the oil vehicle is difficult and often the esterified compounds chromatograph poorly. Also for gas chromatographic separation one must first cleave the ester to a free hydroxyl group before most derivatives can be made.

The use of the DEP allows the positive identification in just a few minutes. A small portion of the sample may be dissolved in an organic solvent, applied to the DEP filament, and positively identified using conventional EI spectra. One such example is shown in figure 3, where full scan electron impact mass spectra identifies testosterone cypionate in an injectable pharmaceutical preparation. The steroid ester is partially resolved from the C18 fatty acids of the cottonseed oil vehicle. Mixtures of anabolics frequently found in illicit "cocktails" can be unambiguously identified using the same DEP probe but with MS/MS employed for monitoring the parent-to-daughter transitions characteristic of the suspected steroids.

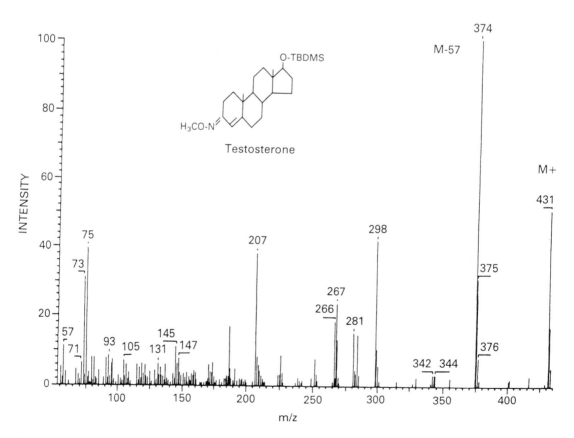

Fig. 3. Electron impact spectrum of testosterone cypionate (top) after partial separation using direct exposure probe. The arrow over the first peak in the reconstructed ion chromatogram (bottom) indicates where the selected scan was obtained.

HIGH-PERFORMANCE LIQUID CHROMATOGRAPHY

High performance liquid chromatography (HPLC) is an attractive alternative to GC because of the possibility of greatly simplifying sample preparation and even the elimination of derivatization steps. In several studies HPLC has been successfully used to separate and screen for the presence of particular steroids, drugs of abuse and the structurally diverse class of compounds, the diuretics. The normal therapeutic dose for many of these drugs is sufficiently large to give rise to relatively high urinary concentrations, thus making HPLC particularly useful for screening purposes. However the possibility of co-eluting peaks and the lack of specificity of most detection systems has required additional analysis by GC/MS to provide unequivocal identification.

A mass spectrometer as a detector for a HPLC system has long been recognized as the ideal combination for providing high resolution analysis of compounds which are involatile or thermally unstable (Ref 8). The basic incompatibility between the high liquid flow of HPLC and the high vacuum requirements of MS has presented considerable problems with interfacing the two techniques. One of the first approaches to the problem was to simply evaporate fractions of the HPLC eluate off-line or remove solvents by heating on a moving wire or belt prior to ionization. The problems with these first generation interfaces were numerous and the use of LC/MS as a routine tool has not gained widespread acceptance. The potential advantages of HPLC/MS for the direct analysis of intact sulfate conjugates was illustrated in a recent report which used an ion spray HPLC/MS interface (Ref.9). Using LC/MS/MS with only minimal preparation of urine samples, these authors were able to obtain full-scan daughter ion spectra of boldenone sulfate up to 17 days after a therapeutic dose of boldenone undecylenate to a horse. Recently there have been such significant advances made in both the HPLC technology and interface designs of commercially available mass spectrometers that in the near future HPLC/MS may become as routine as benchtop-GC/MS is currently.

CONCLUDING REMARKS: EMERGING TECHNOLOGY

The reports of novel instrumentation from fundamental research laboratories represent the foundation for the routine analytical tools of the future. Scientists involved in clinical application laboratories must stay informed of the rapid changes in instrument technology. Their interest and collaborative efforts is essential if these techniques are to evolve into practical applications for solving complex analytical problems. Only when such techniques are proven to be superior to existing techniques will they become commercially viable and their full potential realized.

REFERENCES

1. A. Farjam, G.J. De Jong, R.W. Frei, U.A. Th. Brinkman, W. Haasnoot, A.R.M. Hamers, R. Schilt and F.A. Huf, J. Chromatogr. Sci., 452,419-433 (1988).

2. J. Allison and R.M. Stepnowski, Anal. Chem. 59,1072A-1088A (1987).

3. S.A.McLuckey, G.L.Glish, K.G. Asano and G.J. Van Berkel, Anal. Chem. 60, 2314-2317 (1988).

4. K.L. Busch, G.L. Glish and S.A. Mcluckey. In Mass Spectrometry/Mass Spectrometry: Techniques and Applications of Tandem Mass Spectrometry, VHC New York (1988).

5. M. Kinter, J.R. Shipe and J. Savory. Clin. Chem 34,2178 (1988).

6. D.H. Smith, C. Djerassi, K.H. Mauer and U. Rapp, J. Amer. Chem. Soc. 96,3482 (1974).

7. H.O. Brotherton and R.A. Yost, Anal. Chem 55,549-553 (1983).

8. C. Eckers and J.D. Henion, In Therapeutic Drug Monitoring and Toxicology by Liquid Chromatography, p. 115, Marcel Dekker, New York (1985).

9. L.O.C. Weidolf, E.D. Lee and J.D.Henion, Biomed. Environ. Mass Spectrometry. 15,283-290 (1988).

Drug testing in baseball

Michael M. Lubran

Pathology Department, Harbor–UCLA Medical Center, Torrance, CA 90509, USA

Abstract — The drug program in baseball was started in 1985 after the publicity arising from the involvement of some baseball players in the sale and use of drugs of abuse in 1984. The principal objectives of the policy are the health, welfare and safety of those who work in the game and the maintenance of the integrity of baseball. The program covers club owners, full–time management and administrative personnel employed in professional baseball, Major League and National Association managers, coaches, trainers and umpires, and all N. A. players. Major League players, as a class, are not covered, but specific players, named by the Commissioner, are tested. Many Major League clubs have their own testing programs. The drugs tested for are cocaine, marijuana, heroin and morphine (and other opiates, if abused) and PCP. Experience has shown that these constitute the majority of drugs abused in baseball. The testing program involves unannounced collection of urine from players and other personnel, selected at random by a designated member of the N.A. club. Samples are collected shortly before the game, under visual inspection. The usual procedures of identification and security of the sample are followed and players etc. sign a consent form. Anonymity is maintained throughout and results kept confidential. No disciplinary action is taken for first–time offenders; evaluation, counselling and repeat testing are carried out. Drug testing is carried out in one laboratory. All positive screening results are confirmed by quantitative GC/MS. Blinds are introduced with players' specimens as part of the quality control program.

ORGANIZATION OF BASEBALL

Baseball is played in the United States and some other countries in the summer. Each team is composed nominally of nine players, but it may in fact contain over twenty players, because of the use of substitutes. In addition to the players, the club includes a manager, coaches, trainers and other staff. In professional baseball, each club is owned by an individual or group of people and is operated, like any other business, for profit. The owners voluntarily appoint and pay for a Commissioner, with powers to oversee and regulate all aspects of professional baseball.

Professional baseball is organized into two Major Leagues and groups of teams collectively known as the minor leagues. The Major Leagues, so–called because they played in major cities in the United States, consist of the National League of 12 teams and the American League of 14 teams. Each league has one Canadian team. The National Association consists of 50 minor league teams grouped into classes named triple A (or AAA), double A (or AA), and A. These teams are affiliated to Major League teams and heavily subsidized by them. The minor league teams act as farms, from which the Major League teams can draw players. Within each minor league class, teams are grouped into geographical areas. For example, there are an Eastern League, Southern League, California League and so on. All Major League teams and the minor leagues come under the control of the Commissioner.

ORIGIN OF THE DRUG TESTING PROGRAM

The drug testing program in Baseball was started in July 1985. It covers Major League club owners, all full—time administrative and management personnel employed in professional baseball, all Major League and National Association managers, coaches, trainers and umpires, all National Association Players, and those players disciplined by the Commissioner in February 1986. These players were identified when a Federal Grand Jury in Pittsburgh revealed its findings in May 1985 about a drug case involving baseball players (ref. 1) . In a previous case in 1983 (ref. 2) , four Major League players were sentenced to 91 days in Federal prison for possession of cocaine. During the trials, many players stated in evidence that drug taking, particularly cocaine, was widespread among baseball players in nearly all the 26 Major League teams, and had been so for several years. The Major League Baseball Players Association opposed the inclusion of all Major League players in the drug testing program. However, some Major League clubs have their own programs and can request voluntary testing for suspect players. The penalties imposed by the Commissioner in the Pittsburgh case were severe and included a fine, voluntary community service and regular drug testing throughout their professional careers. The Commissioner can also subject to disciplinary action any player or official convicted of a criminal charge related to a controlled substance.

DRUG PANEL

Drug taking in sports is not new. The desire to win in national and international competitions has led many athletes to take drugs to improve their performance or endurance or to steady their nerves. Many amateur sports organizations consider drug taking to confer an unfair advantage on the athlete, although the supposedly beneficial effect of drugs is still being investigated. The governing bodies of the amateur sports organizations have produced lists of barred drugs and instituted drug testing policies and procedures to ensure compliance with the rules (ref. 3) . The list issued by the US Olympic Committee names more than 140 drugs. It is comprehensive because of the variety of sports covered. Other sports organizations may have shorter lists, restricted to the drugs most likely to be used in that sport.

Because the sports organizations deal with amateurs, who must belong to the organization in order to compete, they are able to mandaté a drug testing program and to enforce it. The situation is different in professional sport, and different for each sport. In professional baseball, the terms and conditions of service of Major League players are embodied in guaranteed contracts with the team organization. Inclusion of a drug testing provision is negotiable. Unless agreed by the Major Leagues Baseball Players Association, drug testing cannot be made mandatory for all players. The situation in the minor leagues is different and a mandatory program has been instituted. The drugs to be tested for in baseball are few, and are limited to those which experience has shown to be used the most. Currently, they include cocaine, marijuana, heroin and related drugs, and phencyclidine (PCP), the first two accounting for most of the usage. Other drugs may be added if they prove to be abused.

BASEBALL DRUG POLICY

The principal concerns of the Commissioner in regard to a drug policy are the health, welfare and safety of the players and maintenance of the integrity of baseball. Players taking the barred drugs before or during a game may be a menace to themselves and other members of the team. As an example of this, one player has recounted how he made a dangerous head—first slide to first base flat on his stomach to prevent breakage of a vial of cocaine in his hip pocket. The image of baseball is tarnished each time a drug taking player makes the news. There is a tendency for newswriters to rehash old cases and the public may get the impression that the problem is more serious than it really is.

The purpose of detection of drug takers is not punishment. It is believed that the program will act as a deterrent to drug taking (ref.4) . There is no disciplinary action or penalty for first time offenders. Results of the drug tests are kept confidential and are known only to the medical advisor of the program, who may refer the offender for counselling, drug education and use prevention, evaluation and, if required, treatment. Club and league management are not advised of the results. Second offenders are treated on a case by case basis. If a player refuses a urine test, his name is sent to the Commissioner's Office and to the Major League team of which his club is an affiliate. The other part of the program is education. All organizations have employee assistance programs, which can carry out this function as well as assisting in rehabilitation. Recently, Baseball has produced a booklet describing the harmful effects of certain drugs. The booklet, printed in English and Spanish, is to be distributed to all players in major and minor leagues and appropriate officials and other staff.

SCREENING PROGRAM

Selection of individuals
In the Major Leagues, all of the penalty players (i.e. known drug abusers) and players being

rehabilitated are tested twice yearly. Testing is usually carried out at the ballparks; no advance notice is given. All of the 50 minor league teams (24 AAA, 16 AA and 10 A) are tested twice during the year at the ballpark. Each person on the roster is assigned a number and a designated official of each team (the trainer or team manager) draws numbers at random to identify the subjects to be tested. It was logistically impossible to collect samples from more than 10 people at one session. Personnel of the office of the Commissioner are tested once during the year, including management and staff.

Collection of urine

The designated official is informed of the impending visit of the urine collection team 24 hours before the visit. Urine is collected before the beginning of the game. Ideally, it should be collected at the end of the game, but practical considerations make this impossible. Teams have to leave soon after the game and can not tolerate the delay of two or three hours required for urine collection.

Urine is collected using the method which proved successful in the Summer Olympics held in Los Angeles in 1984. The person being tested is identified by the management official,his name is entered on a specially designed form and he is given an identification number. He enters any medication he has taken during the preceding three days and signs a release permitting the collection of urine and its analysis. The copy of the form which is sent to the laboratory performing the analyses carries only the identification number. The part of the form bearing the name is sent to the one authorized doctor, who is also the only person receiving the test results from the laboratory. The subject selects a plastic urine container sealed in a wrapping from a number available and takes it into the lavatory. After unwrapping the container himself, he urinates into it, under the direct view of a member of the collecting team. In the case of the small number of females tested, a female views the collection. For the men, the collection is supervised by a male. The subject selects two polyethylene bottles from a number available, pours about 75 ml of urine into each and closes each bottle with a plastic screw cap. The bottles are each tagged with an adhesive label bearing the same identification number and placed in a specially designed case, which is closed and sealed with a plastic strip carrying the identification number. Labels with the same number are attached to the forms and copies, thus providing positive identification. The design of the case ensures that it can not be opened without breaking the plastic seal, thus providing a guarantee against tampering. The whole procedure is witnessed by the subject, who then signs a form indicating that he is satisfied with the procedure. The cases are put into a large container and sent without delay by air to the laboratory. They are not packed in dry ice or other cold material.

The purpose of this elaborate procedure is to make sure that the urine collected came from the named person and was not contaminated by him or by the collecting team. It also ensures confidentiality of the subject and integrity of the sample at all stages. The procedure was designed to stand up to legal challenge. The form received by the laboratory becomes a link in the chain of custody.

Laboratory examination

All urine specimens are tested by the same commercial laboratory, which was selected because of its excellent record of urine drug analyses, its highly qualified staff and superior quality control program. The specimens received from Baseball are handled separately from the others. In the receiving area, the cases are opened and the integrity of the seals confirmed. The specimens are given a laboratory

identification number and one of the two containers is placed, unopened, in a freezer at $-20^{\circ}C$, to be kept for one year. A chain of custody form is generated, and accompanies the remaining specimen until all stages of the analysis are completed and the results reported. The receiving area and the analytical laboratories are secured, only authorized personnel being admitted. In the analytical area, the specimen is examined visually for abnormal appearance and its pH and specific gravity measured using test papers. Aliquots are removed for screening and the container then closed and placed in a refrigerator. The Emit procedure is used for the screening tests, using the manufacturer's cutoff values except for THC, which is screened at 20 ng/ml. Positive tests are confirmed using GC/MS and selective ion monitoring. In most cases, deuterated compounds are used as internal standards. The concentration of the drug is reported, not just an arbitrary positive or negative. Decision limits for the presence of drugs are : benzoylecgonine 100 ng/ml, THC 10 ng/ml, opiates (as morphine) 240 ng/ml and PCP 25 ng/ml.

Quality control

In addition to the extensive quality quality program run by the laboratory, blind samples are submitted on a regular basis with the Baseball specimens. The blinds are normal urines spiked with the drugs or their metabolites at various concentrations and are submitted with approprite documentation as if they were actual specimens. Occasionally, drug—free normal urines are used as blinds.

LOGISTICS

teams of three health professionals are used for each visit in the Minor Leagues. Initially, the same professionals travelled to all the. baseball parks. Later, it was possible to train more people and to use teams based on regions. For the Major Leagues, teams of one to three professionals are used, depending on the number of players to be tested. Collection teams spend two to three hours at each ball park, and urine from bothhome team and visitors is collected. Careful planning permits the collecting teams to test each team twice during the baseball season.

CONCLUSIONS

The Baseball drug testing program appears to have achieved its major goals. It has been a deterrent. The number of new positive urines has been small and has remained small. Repeat positives are very few. Drug education programs are active in Major and Minor Leagues. However, because we are living in a drug oriented society, continued vigilance, including a comprehensive drug screening program, is still required to keep drugs out of baseball.

REFERENCES

1. P. Axthelm, Newsweek, 106, 64–65 (1985).
2. F. Lidz, Sports Illustrated, 60, 9 (1984).
3. J.C. Wagner, Am. J. Hosp. Pharmacy, 44, 305–310 (1987).
4. M. Chass, Sporting News, 203, 24 (1987).

Doping in Italy

M. Marigo, G. Menini

Institute of Legal Medicine, University of Verona 37134,
Italy

Abstract - The authors have made a general outline of doping
in sporting events, referring particularly to Italy. Some
consideration is given to the list of prohibited substances
issued by the IOC. A brief description of the legislative
regulations and problems concerning doping in athletes is
also discussed. The report states the actual medical and
legal criteria used in Italy and conclude with reference to
general sport ethics.

DEFINITION

Doping is the administering or use of any physiological substance by an
athlete whether during competition or training: taken either in abnormal
quantity or introduced in the body via unnatural routes with the sole inten-
tion of increasing artificial and disloyal gains during any competition.
(International Olympic Committee - IOC)

THE SUBSTANCES USED

The following forms of doping exist:
Chemical doping: (i.e. amphetamines);
Hormonal doping (i.e. anabolic steroids with: testosterone, growth hormone
and similar hormonal substances:;
Haemodoping and doping with hypnosis.
The CIO has recently (1985) updated the list of prohibited substances which
appears on table 1.

Other drugs not listed with the prohibited substances but, however, still
considered as doping agents are: Fructose 1,6 diphosphate (esaphosphine)
which stimulates the catabolism of glucose; creatine phosphate (neoton), a
high caloric compound which acts a biologic accumulator of chemical energy
derived from oxidative breakdown of sugars; creatinol phosphate (aplodan)
similar to the former, the alpha-keto-glutarate of pyridoxine which enhances
oxidative metabolism in muscle by acting on oxidative phosphorylation; 1-
carnitine which by transferring the free fatty acids (FFA) activated by the
cytoplasm to the mitochondria supplies energy by lipid metabolism (the most
advantageous) and impedes toxic-storage of fatty acids; cytildiphosphocoline
(neuroton) which combats hyposine; the corticosuprarenal extracts stimulating
antiasthenic action; taurine which improves functional metabolism in cardiac
cell during hypoxia and/or anoxia; high doses of vitamin C and E considering
their antioxidative action and high doses of ubidecarenon which regulates the
electronic transport in mitochondria (27,29). All these substances,
metabolic in nature, may be useful not only for increasing sport performance
but also for restoring metabolic energy and in addition facilitate excretion
of toxic endogenous catabolites. Finally it is worthwhile mentioning a range
of products whose use is prohibited both by sport legislations and penal law;
they are namely narcotics. In the USA it has been proven that many professional athletes in baseball, in American football and basketball consume large
quantities of drugs for maintaining top performance. Cocaine with its sadly
famous "Snowballings" is among the most popular products in use (27). In
North American colleges the athletes use marijuana (20%), "fute" tobacco
(16%), cocaine (7%), but most popular is alcohol (65%). Like any other substance introduced into the body, drugs often cause adverse side effects in
addition to their therapeutic effect.

TABLE 1. Indicative list of prohibited substances (IOC, 1985)

Sympathomimetic amines
    Chlorprenaline
    Ephedrine
    Etafedrine
    Isoetharine
    Isoprenaline
    Methoxyphenamine
    Methylephedrine
    Related compounds

Psychomotor Stimulants
    Amphetamine
    Benzphetamine
    Chlorphentermine
    Cocaine
    Diethylpropin
    Dimethylamphetamine
    Ethylamphetamine
    Fencamfamin
    Meclofenoxate
    Methylamphetamine
    Methylphenidate
    Norpseudoephedrine
    Pemoline
    Phendimetrazine
    Phentermine
    Pipradol
    Prolintane

Stimulants of CNS
    Amiphenazole
    Bemigride
    Caffeine
    Cropropamide
    Crotethamide
    Doxapram
    Ethamivan
    Leptazol
    Nikethamide
    Picrotoxin
    Strychnine

Beta-blockers
    Alprenolol
    Atenolol
    Labetalol
    Metoprolol
    Nadolol
    Oxprenolol
    Propranolol
    Sotalol
    Related compounds

Narcotic analgesics
    Alfa-prodine
    Anileridine
    Codeine
    Dihydrocodeine
    Dipipanone
    Ethylmorphine

    Heroin
    Hydrocodone
    Hydromorphone
    Levorphanol
    Morphine
    Oxycodone
    Oxymorphone
    Pentazocine
    Meperidine
    Phenazocine
    Piminodine
    Thebacon
    Trimeperidine

Anabolic steroids
    Bolasterone
    Boldenone
    Clostebol
    Dehydrochlormethyl-
        Testosterone
    Fluoxymesterone
    Mesterolone
    Methenolone
    Methandienone
    Methyltestosterone
    Nandrolone
    Oxymesterone
    Oxymetholone
    Stanazolol
    Testosterone

Diuretics
    Acetazolamide
    Amiloride
    Bendrofluazide
    Benzthiazide
    Bumetanide
    Canrenone
    Chlormerodrine
    Chlorthalidone
    Dichlorofenamide
    Ethacrynic Acid
    Furosemide
    Hydrochlorothiazide
    Spironolactone
    Triamterene
    Related compounds

Obviously, the major effect of a drug is different according to its molecular composition, which is why some drugs are tolerated more than others. Referring to those drugs listed in the table, it may be noted amphetamines remove signs of fatigue. In altering a perfectly normal physiological response, they may in fact produce a disease which is not always completely curable. Because of slow and incomplete recovery, there have been cases where athletes have even died. Drug addiction, cardio-vascular disorders, cardiac arrhythmias, and the possibility of death are among the poisonous effects of amphetamine. The beta-blockers may give rise to bradycardia, increase peripherial vascular and bronchial resistance and increase serum potassium.

Anabolic steroid bring about short term effects which are psychological in nature such as high spirits, a feeling of well being, irritability, and irritability, and increased appetite. Long term doses may have dangerous effects on brain development in infants in particular to centers responsible for sexual development, especially in women. In males they often induce the early onset of puberty, azo and/or oligospermia, testicular atrophy, increased or reduced libido. In females they may cause irregular menstruation, masculinity, acne and a long series of other metabolic alterations (3,4,8,14 15,22).

The diuretics cause dehydration and loss of sodium and potassium including asthenia, arrhythmias and also abulia. Growth hormone causes acromegaly, diabetes and likely formation of antibodies which may alter response to the drug. Haemodoping can provoke a series of hazards which are all peculiar to transfusions; namely the risk of viral hepatitis, AIDS, malaria, syphilis and moreover the remote danger of anaphylaxis following use of incompatible blood, are all events worth bearing in mind. With self haemodoping, signs of cardiovascular insufficiency due to over-loading may occur, (not yet reported); if repeated, there may be storage of iron in the tissues and micro circulatory disorders due to the increased blood volume (10,23,28).

DOPING AND SPORTS

The first confirmed death, resulting from the abuse of stimulants, dates from 1886: in the Bordeaux race, the death of the English cyclist Linton in Paris followed a mixture of heroin administered by his trainer (24). After the death of the Danish cyclist Knud Jensen during the 1960 Rome Olympics, traces of amphetamine were reported at autopsy. The IOC have published a resolution which prohibits drugs which heighten performance in sport. It is to be emphasized that in 1960 the control of antidoping was limited to athletes engaged in the Olympics and authorized only exams aimed at identifying drugs such as CNS stimulants and narcotics. In 1967 Tommy Simpson died during the "Tour de France," while cycling up Mont Ventoux during a scorching afternoon in July having abused drugs to combat fatigue. In 1970 the anabolic steroids were included in the list of prohibited drugs and their control became extended not only to the Olympics but also international and national competitions. In 1974 Pelle Svensonn, winner of a silver medal at the Tokyo Olympics, made an open confession to the use of anabolic substances. The review "Nature" has reported that within 30 years (1952-82), 59 Russian competitors in the Olympics have died. The mortality rate among the latter is 17% compared to 4.5% in the USA and 2.1% among the British, according to the Soviet Sport Review. Some individuals believe that there may be a connection between this high mortality rate and the extent of anabolic steroid abuse during training.

In 1983 testosterone, diuretics, caffeine, beta-inhibitors were added to the list of prohibited or highly unrecommendable drugs (20). In 1985 the post-mortem carried out on the Dutch middle distance runner Augustinius Jaspers (competitor at the L.A. Olympics), revealed that the athlete had taken an overdose of anabolic steroids. In 1985 growth hormones and haemodoping were included in the prohibited list. The fact that 200 meters Italian champion Pietro Mennea during an interview with the "Repubblica" (23.08.1987), affirms "I admit to have taken somatotrophine" does confirm that the use of prohibited drugs is extremely common and wide-spread not only among athletes but also in others. This conclusion is based on the statement made by Professor Romano Tordelli, coach for Italian middle distance runners for over 15 years. His statement created an enormous turmoil in the world of Italian athletics, on the eve of the world finals in Rome (August 1987). According to Tordelli, many athletes use illegal drugs following the guidelines suggested by the federal technicians. The "remedy" is set by the doctors of the Federation. In particular Dr. Faraggiana, one of the 3 officials of the Italian team at the World Games in Rome on behalf of the FIDAL (Federozione Italiana Di Atletica Leggera) arranges the supply of anabolic steroids and testosterone for athletes and technicians (7,18).

The laws governing blood tests and examination of urine aimed at the control of anti-doping are quoted in the Parliamentary Act (D.M.) passed 5th July, 1975, the chief regulation stating as follows: the collection of urine is to be carried out by the doctor appointed by the FMSI (Italian Sport Medicine Federation) on athletes selected or defined with other criteria. The procedure must be carried out in the presence of the health superintendent. Athletes must undergo a medical check-up and are compelled to declare any medications taken within the preceding 5 days. In all circumstaces, they may be assisted by the doctor of the association to which they belong (9). The liquid specimen obtained (50 cc) is to be placed in 2 numbered containers (each number pertaining to the athlete) and sent to the FMSI laboratory (Florence or Rome). The refusal of an athlete to cooperate with these procedures is considered positive evidence of doping. There is no precise time-limit regarding micturition which in cases may be aided by administering liquids but not drugs. In conclusion, there are forms which must be signed by the doctor in charge, the doctor who recovers the athlete and the athlete himself. In the laboratory, the material is analyzed according to the qualitative and quantitative criteria employing the various methods such as gas chromatography, RIA (radio immunoassays) and thin layer paper chromatography (17,21,25).

LEGISLATIONS CONCERNING DOPING

At the 1983 Pan American Games held in Caracas, 17 athletes were disqualified and 11 more withdrew so as to avoid the gas chromatography test. At the 1984 L.A. Olympics, the silver medal for the 10,000 meters awarded to the Finnish long-distance runner Martti Vainio was confiscated as he was found positive in the anti-doping testing. The same destiny befell Sandra Gasser, Swiss middle distance runner and bronze medal winner in the 1500 meters at the world finals in Rome. Twelve cases of doping with similar disqualifications at the world championship of modern pentathlon held at Montecatini (Italy, 1987), have been reported. These are probably the most outstanding among a series of examples which justify the need for strict regulation for athletes who use illegal drugs. However, what exactly does the law state? Previously, in 1964 some CONI Federations (Football, Canoeing, Cycling, Basketball and Boxing) were covered by the FMSI (Italian Sport Medicine Federation) rules for antidoping detection. In cases of violation, solely sports penalties are imposed out of respect for sport ethics. At the International level it is wise to bear in mind that in France the first laws concerning doping were passed in 1965, Belgium in 1966, Germany, Austria, Switzerland and Great Britain in 1967, and finally Argentina in 1969. In Italy, the first official (2) legislations regulating doping dates back to 1971 with the code of law number 1099 enacted on the 26th of October, which was aimed at the general discipline regarding sport activities. Article 3 of the said law states: "Athletes taking part in sport competitions who indulge in the use of substances which might endanger their health in attempt to artificially modify their natural resources, are liable to punishment. Whosoever administers to athletes who participate in sport competitions the above mentioned substances with the aim of artificially improving their natural resources is guilty." Following the latter no other laws have been approved with the exception of the law passed (31.05.1985) by the former Minister of Health Costante Degan which made illegal the practice of haemodoping in the world of sport (17,21, 25). As for as the legislation strictly pertaining to sports, it should be pointed out that while the IOC is responsible for the international organization of all the various initiatives, it delegates the sanctions against doping offenders to investigations carried out by the international or national federation specifically responsible for the competitions. Generally speaking, the sport legislations are as follows:
a) Annulment of result;
b) Disqualification or expulsion from any sport activity for a given period of time;
c) Pecuniary penalty.

MEDICAL AND LEGAL CONSIDERATIONS

Every discussion on doping deserves at least two considerations:
1) The use of drug is evidence of attempted fraud against the competing colleague; thus violating every principle of sport ethics;
2) Making use of doping substances means breech of sport regulations and where they exist, breaking laws based on penal code with far more serious consequences than a simple suspension from official sport activities and even detention. If prior to or during a competition an athlete takes substances capable of modifying his actual condition he renders himself in an abnormal state compared to his opponents (sport unloyalty) and is capable of "artificial" performances due to the administration of these substances. It is worthwhile mentioning that in any case the drugs must be adequately monitored by experts; failure to do so besides giving momentary benefit may well lead to a series of consequences permanent in nature. Unfortunately, in a world made of records and moments of praise, it is not unusual to encounter a technician or doctor who guarantees or promises the result only under certain circumstances, through which the athlete unknowingly compromises himself for a step higher in the rostrum. However, it is unpardonable to discover the

presence of illegal substances in athletes who have actually taken the drug, not for improving their performance but for treating a state of pathology. It may well be that prior to the event, the athlete was afflicted by slight or momentary ailment (bronchitis, colds, boils or small anal abscesses etc.) the nature of which does not impede competing, but is however sufficient to interfere with the expected performance in that athletic field. In this case the use of appropriate known drugs permits exceeding the limits imposed by the ailment, at least for the duration of the competition. It is obvious in my opinion that the athlete, who is wisely advised by his doctor, must make provisions for his needs, avoiding the substances which are listed in table 1. This should not require too much effort since the official pharmaceutical guide lists a variety of recommended and efficient alternatives to banned substances.

The use of "dope" by athletes does not seem to be, or rather, is not reported to be, exceptionally high in Italy. In other countries, particularly the USA, abuse is very common both in athletes from "colleges" and among extremely well-paid professionals of American baseball or basketball. In a recent investigation carried out by Gledhill (28), of 1800 athletes completing an anonymous questionnaire, about 13% admitted to the use of narcotics. It is wise to bear in mind that the Ministry of Health law passed in 1985 prohibits the use of haemodoping and makes illegal, since the use of haemodoping is considered another yet another form of doping.

REFERENCES

1. R. Guillet, J. Genety, Le doping de l'homme e du cheval, Masson Ed., Ed. Paris, France, (1965).
2. J. Vacher, H. Perie, J.M. Fourre, Aspects medico-legaux de la medicine du sport, Ed. Masson, Paris, France, (1969).
3. J. Money, A.A. Emrhardt, Man and woman, boy and girl. The John Hopkins University Press. Baltimore, USA, (1972).
4. J.P. Pelizza, Contribution a l'etude des anabolisants et de leur emploi en pratique sportive, These Paris, France, (1972).
5. F.J. Buick, N. Gledhill, A.B. Froses, L. Spriet, E.C. Meyers, J. Appl. Physiol., UK, 48, 636, (1980).
6. R. Guillet, J Genety, Brunet, E. Guedj, Medicina dello Sport, Masson Ed. Milano, Italy, (1980).
7. L. Montanaro, Le doping, information et prevention, UCI, France, (1980).
8. L. Spriet, N. Gledhill, A.B. Froses, D.L. Wilkes, E.C. Meyers, Med. Scien. Sport Exer, UK, 12, 122 (1980).
9. A. Bencine, R. Cagliesi Cingolari, Arch. Med. Leg. Ass., Italy, 4, 49-56 (1982).
10. A. Franchi, G. Marena, Monografia, FMSI, Roma, Italy, (1982).
11. N. Gledhill, Med. Scien. Sport Exer., UK, 14 (1982).
12. G. Marena, A. Franchi, Medicina dello Sport, Italy, 36, 151-153 (1983).
13. Athletes and androgenes, Pharos, 47, 32-37 (1984).
14. K. Berg, Chemical Sports medicine, USA, 3, 779-789 (1984).
15. H.A. Haupt, G.D. Rovere, American J. of Sports Medicine, USA, 12, 469-484 (1984).
16. D.R. Lamb, American J. of Sports Medicine, USA, 12, 31-38 (1984).
17. L. Palmieri, Medicina Legale dello Sport., ESI, Napoli, Italy, (1984).
18. G. Smith, Sport e Medicina, Italy, 5, 25-27 (1984).
19. H.G. Klein, Blood doping, New England, UK, 13, 854 (1985).
20. R.H. Strauss, Columbus Press., Ohio, USA, (1985).
21. F. Antoniotti, N.M. Di Luca, Lineamenti di medicina legale e delle assicurazioni nello sport. SEU, Roma, Italy, (1986).
22. A. Chapelle, JAMA, USA, 14, 942-945 (1986).
23. F. Marzatico, Atletica Studi, Italy, 4/5, 323-346 (1986).
24. S. Meda, Doctor, Italy, 2, 80-83 (1986).
25. Tutela sanitaria delle attivita sportive, Notizie Sanita 85, n.6, Regione Lombardia, Italy, (1986).
26. A. Ciarambino, Medicus, Italy, 7-9 (01.04.1987).
27. D.B. Clement, Sport e Medicina, Italy, 3, 17-23 (1987).
28. N. Gledhill, Sport e Medicina, Italy, 3, 30-33 (1987).
29. E. Marmo, Rassegna Internazionale di Medicina dello Sport, Italy, 7, 1-5 (1987).

Regular checking of sportsmen at all levels of competition

Lars Josefsson and Johan Larsen

Department of Biochemistry C, University of Copenhagen, and
School of Hospital Technicians, DK-2200 Copenhagen N, Denmark

The use of drugs among high level sportsmen/women is a phenomenon we have known about for a rather long time, particularly among those active in power sports, such as weight lifting and the various athletic throwing events. The increased competition created by the involvement of more sponsors and higher prize money, as well as national pride, has helped spread the use of drugs during the last decades not only into new sport branches, but also to the common sportsperson. Therefore actions have been taken in most of our countries to prevent the doping. Although the approaches may differ significantly from one country to another, there has been a general increase in efforts to solve the problems.

In Denmark the Danish Sport Federation has taken responsibility for doping control since 1978. The Danish Sport Federation, which includes 53 special sport associations comprised of more than 1.7 million members, has delegated the doping control matters to a special Doping Control Committee. The Doping Control Committee presently has 10 members: 5 physicians, a pharmacist, a lawyer, and 3 sports leaders.

The duties of the committee includes:

1. The preparation and distribution of information about the problems of doping to all the various sport associations, and to provide a current list of the drugs available in Denmark.

2. Administration and performance of doping control in all aspects.

3. Representation of the Danish Sport Federation internationally in doping matters.

4. The development of programs for cooperation with other nations, particularly the other Nordic countries, to strengthen its actions.

Since its creations, the Danish Doping Control Committee has performed and administrated more than 1,000 doping controls of sportsmen/women, representing more than half of the 53 different sport associations. Most of the control samples have been taken from sportsmen/women active in the sport branches where the use of drugs are most common, i.e. weight lifting, cycling and wrestling.

Occasionally the Doping Control Committee has also taken control samples at training camps and at competitions in sport branches not expected to have a high probability of drug use. This is done to emphasize that the committee has the capacity to oversee all the sport branches and to control sportsmen/women even at the junior level.

The regulations adopted in Denmark were originally based on the work done by the International Olympic Committee. The present regulations have evolved largely from the cooperative efforts of the other Nordic countries. Last year this cooperation resulted in a single set of regulations for doping control which were adopted by all the Nordic countries.

These regulations, after being ratified by each of the separate Nordic Sport Federations, is now available in a printed document and has been distributed to all Nordic Sport Clubs. The goal of these regulations has been to collect and define a set of principles or minimum standards which are valid for all the doping control work. At the same time, it was necessary to maintain a degree of flexibility demanded by the differences in organization of the sport associations from the various Nordic countries. This common Nordic regulation about doping control will, when properly adopted, secure the legal rights of the individual sportsman/woman, secure coordination between international and national jurisdiction, and open up cooperative control measures.

EXCERPTS OF RULES FROM THE COMMON REGULATIVE OF THE NORDIC
NATIONAL SPORT FEDERATIONS ABOUT DOPING CONTROL

1. Use of drugs on the banned drug list or any other kind of doping is prohibited at competitions as well as during training.

    The prohibition list of IOC constitutes the basis both in relation to means and procedures.

    Instigation or assistance to the use of doping is prohibited.

2. Doping control can be undertaken on every sportsman/woman, who is a member of an association of the National Sport Federation. Animals used in competitions are also subject to doping control.

    The doping control, which can be undertaken without any advance notice, can be done at any time at training or competition.

    Control of national sportsmen/women, who are active in foreign countries, can be undertaken by the foreign sport authorities after agreement.

3. Doping control shall be executed according to valid rules. Each of the National Federations can specify more detailed rules for the execution of the testing.

4. Every sportsman/woman, who is selected for testing under doping control, has a duty to accept.

5. If a sportsman/woman is judged guilty of doping, he/she shall be excluded from all competitions for a minimum of 18 months for the first violation. A more severe punishment will accompany a second violation.

6. A person, who instigates a sportsman/woman to doping, shall be excluded for a minimum of 5 years from competition and from every commission related to associations of the National Sport Federation.

7. Violation of the doping rules shall be handled according to the following principles:

    a. The accusing and judging bodies shall be separate.

    b. Everyone accused shall have opportunity to respond to a written accusation.

    c. Every case must be presented accurately, and reasonable doubts shall be to the credit of the accused.

    d. The decision in the case and the justification for the decision shall be given to the accused in writing.

    e. It shall be possible to appeal against the decision to a higher tribunal. The convicted shall be informed about this possibility.

    f. As a temporary measure, the person who is handling a case, can suspend the athletes found guilty of doping.

CONCERNING THE DOPING CONTROL

There are specific guidelines for the sample acquisition and analysis which include:

1. The control group, which shall contain at least 2 persons.

2. Notice of the control at the place of control.

3. Selection of actives according to their ranking and/or to drawing of lots.

4. Summons to the doping stations. The summons must be in writing and it shall be delivered when the competition is finished.

5. The location and usage of the premises for the doping control.

6. The execution of the control.

    a. The organizer of the assembly shall assist at the control.

    b. The athlete is allowed to be accompanied by an attendant, but other unauthorized persons are not permitted in the control station.

    c. The athlete shall deliver 50-100 ml urine under observation.

    d. The athlete must be able to identify him/herself to the control collection team.

    e. The athlete may select for him/herself the container for the urine sample and witness the process of dividing and sealing the urine sample in the glass ampoules.

    f. The sample glass ampoules shall be distinctly marked with a code.

    g. The athlete shall inform about any drug he/she has taken within the last 10 days.

    h. The control group, the athlete and his/her companion shall testify by their signatures that the doping control procedure has been executed correctly.

7. The samples shall be subsequently sent for analysis to one of the IOC accredited laboratories. The samples kept in reserve shall be stored chilled and secured.

Vitakrom–TMN, new phase for the gas chromatography of stimulants in doping control

M. Maksimović, M. Tandara, B.*Nikolin

SBS Factory of drugs,* Faculty of Pharmacy, Doping control laboratory, Sarajevo, Yugoslavia

Abstract - Methods we described for the gas chromatographic determination of stimulation of stimulants and narcotic using the new stationary phase Vitakrom-TMN.

INTRODUCTION

Gas - liquid chromatography has for many years been the method of choice for urine extract screening in doping control. It is very difficult to obtain an ideal stationary phase for screening different classes of doping agents such as stimulants, narcotic analgesics, beta-blockers, diuretics and other compounds by gas chromatography. The new stationary phase Vitakrom-TMN, however, can be used for screening stimulants and narcotic analgesics from the list of doping substances.

MATERIAL AND METHODS

The screening procedure for volatile substances uses 10% Apiezon L + 10% KOH (ref. 1,2) and 10% Apiezon L + 10% KOH + 2% Igepal (ref. 3).

Gas chromatography is carried out using a commercially available instrument (Perkin Elmer, Sigma 2B with Sigma 15 computer), under the following conditions: Injector temperature 250°C, detector temperature 280°C, program 130°C (0 min), 12°C/min, 260°C (6 min,), using a nitrogen phosphorus detector, hydrogen 2.5 ml/min, air 100 ml/min, N_2 12 ml/min.

Vitakrom-TMN is a type of mineral oil obtained by a special technology. The oil is thermally, chemically and oxidative resistant. Vitakrom-TMN has a high boiling point 550°C and very low evaporation heat. The columns 10% Vitakrom-TMN + 2% KOH + 2% Igepal, Supelcoport (100-120 mesh) are prepared, having the length of 2 m x 6 mm and 0.65 m x 6 mm.

Extraction is conducted according to the procedure for volatile substances using dephenylamine as internal standard.

To 5 ml of urine, add 0.5 ml of 5 N KOH, 2.0 ml of freshly distilled ether, containing 5 ppm of internal standard diphenylamine and approximately 3 g of anhydrous sodium sulfate. This mixture is shaken mechanically for 20 minutes and centrifuged at 2000 r.p.m. (ca. 3000 x g) for 5 minutes. Approximately 1.5 ml of the organic phase is used for the measurement.

RESULTS

Based on experiments it was found that the Vitakrom packing provides extended column lifetime, and it reduces the analysis time for some substances. In urine extracts one can detect the occurence of not only parent drug substance but also metabolites (fenfluramine, diethylpropione, nikethamide etc).

Table 1 shows the chromatographic results obtained on column 10% Vitakrom-TMN + 2% KOH + 2% Igepal, Supelcoport (100-120 mesh), 2 m x 6 mm.

TABLE 1.

Substance	R_t (min)	RR_t (min)	Retention index
Amphetamine	4.59	0.765	1389
Codeine	10.16	1.693	1885
Diethylpropione	9.30	1.550	1853
	9.50	1.583	1872
Dimethylamphetamine	4.62	0.770	1397
Diphenylamine	6.00	1.000	1558
Ephedrine	4.52	0.753	1379
Ethylamphetamine	4.70	0.783	1407
Fenfluramine	5.61	0.935	1508
Methylamphetamine	4.60	0.766	1390
Methylephedrine	4.45	0.741	1373
Nicotine	8.10	1.350	1764
Nikethamide	5.49	0.915	1493
Norpseudoephedrine	4.54	0.756	1381
Phendimetrazine	7.50	1.250	1710
Phenmetrazine	7.40	1.233	1702
Pethidine	8.31	1.385	1789

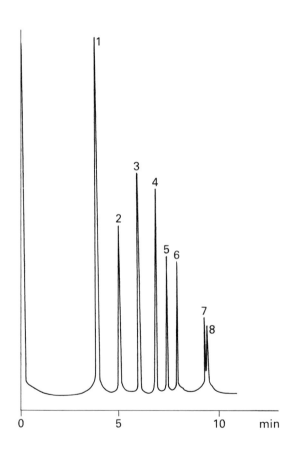

Fig. 1. Chromtogram of urine after extract of diethylpropione oral dose of 50 mg (24 h urine). 1,2,4,5,6 metabolites, 3 diphenylamine, 7 and 8 diethylpropione.

REFERENCES

1. A.H. Beckett, G.T. Tucker and A.C. Moffat, <u>J. Pharm. Pharmac.</u>, <u>19</u>, 273-294 (1967).
2. A.H. Beckett, L.G. Brookes and E.V.B. Shenoy, <u>J. Pharm. Pharmac.</u>, <u>21</u>, Suppl. 151 S - 156 S (1969).
3. M. Donike, R. Iffland and L. Jaenike, <u>Arzeim. - Forsch. (Drug Res.)</u>, 24 (4). 556-560 (1974).

Identification of pemoline in urine

Nenad Bobarević, Sonja Bobarević, *Meliha Lekić, Branko Nikolin

Faculty of Pharmacy, *Faculty of Medicine, University of Sarajevo, Doping control Laboratory, Sarajevo, Yugoslavia

Abstract - All analytical procedures used up to now for identification of pemoline are time consuming and not very reliable for routine drug screening in doping control. High performance liquid chromatography/HPLC/using reversed phase column gives the possibility of identification of pemoline without derivatisation. The purposes of the presented research were to develop a rapid and simple HPLC method for the identification of pemoline and to develop a method free from interferences by all common drugs and substances from the list of forbidden drugs in sport.

INTRODUCTION

The identification of pemoline in biological liquids can be carried out by gas chromatography-mass spectrometry (ref. 1) applied only after hydrolysis and derivatization. The advantage of high-performance liquid chromatography (HPLC) lies in the possibility of identification of determination of pemoline without derivatization (ref. 2-5).

EXPERIMENTAL

The analysis was performed by high-performance liquid chromatograph Series 4 with spectrophotometric detector LC-85, Automatic Sampling System ISS-100, Data Station Sigma 15 and a prepacked 25 cm x 4.6 mm i.d. reversed-phase Analytical C_{18} column (10 µm) (Perkin-Elmer). The mobile phase was phosphate buffer (pH 4.90)-methanol (80:20). The flow rate was 2 ml/min, pressure 18.5-19.5 MPa, column temperature 35°C and detector wavelength 216 mm. Confirmation by GC/MS was performed by gas chromatograph (Dani 3800), mass spectrometer (7070E V.G. Analytical) and fused silica capilary column (SE-54, 12 m x 0.20 mm). GC condictions: 100°C/1 min rising by 16°C/min to 290°C/5 min; T_{inject} = 280°C; He = 2 ml/min; splitless. MS conditions: T_{source} = 220°C EI, 70 eV; full scan.

Sample preparation

An aliquot (1 ml) of the urine, 0.5 g of sodium sulfate, 0.2 g of phosphate buffer (pH 6.9) and 4 ml of chloroform with 8-chlortheophyllline as the internal standard (5 µg/ml) were mixed for 30 sec and centrifuged. The organic phase was evaporated in a stream of nitrogen. The residue was dissolved in 0.5 ml of methanol and 10 µl was injected. The residue was dissolved in 0.5 ml of ethyl acetate for confirmation by GC/MS.

RESULTS

Urine concentration of 1 µg of pemoline/ml can be reliably analyzed by this procedure. In the above analysis, a base-line signal-to-noise ratio of 2 corresponds to a minimum detection limit of 0.5 µg of pemoline/ml. An example of the chromatogram of a mixture of standards and another chromatogram of urine sampled 6 hr after oral administration of 20 mg of pemoline is shown in Fig 1. The mass spectrum of the same sample is shown in Fig 2.

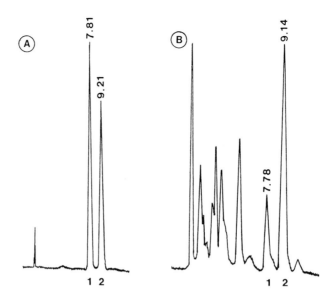

Fig 1. A) Chromatogram of mixture of standards: 1. pemoline,
2.8-Chlortheophylline; B) Chromatogram of urine collected
6 hr after oral administration of 20 mg of pemoline and
spiked with 20 μg/ml of the internal standard.

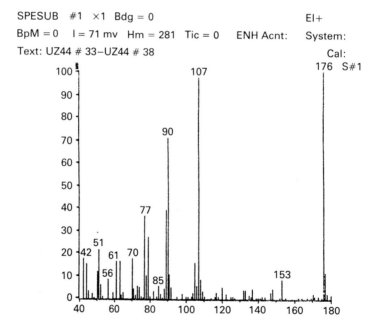

Fig 2. Mass Spectra

REFERENCES

1. M. Van Boven and P. Saenens, J. Chromatog. 134, 415-421 (1977).
2. C.P. Tomkins, S.J. Soldin, S.M. MacLeod, J.G. Rochefort and J.M. Swanson, Therapeutic Drug Monitoring 2, 255-260 (1980).
3. K. Nishihara, Y. Kohda, Y. Saitoh, F. Nakagawa and Y. Honda, Therapeutic Drug Monitoring 6, 232-239 (1984).
4. B. Nikolin, N. Bobarević and S. Lasić, J. Pharm. Biomed. Anal. (in press)
5. N. Bobarevic, S. Lasić and B. Nikolin, Acta Pharm Jugosl. 38, 31-34 (1988).

Open forum

ANALYTICAL ASPECTS OF DRUG TESTING IN COMPETITIVE ATHLETICS

Open Forum Discussions prepared by John Savory and James R. Shipe

Panel Members:
D. A. Cowan Chairman, D. H. Catlin, R. Dugal, H. W. Durbeck, M. Lubran, S. Rendic.

The Chairman introduced the discussion with a few general comments about the purpose of drug screening. Is the purpose the complete control of drug abuse in sport rather than the limited activity of "urine specimen in - result out"? The most important considerations should be the welfare of the athlete and adherence to the rules of the sport. Quality assurance of the entire program is of vital importance particularly the authenticity of the specimen in terms of this specimen reflecting the true situation of the athlete as whether drug taking was involved in the preparation for athletic competition.

The discussion then focussed on the limitations of testing only during competition and not during training. With this type of testing the positive rate is approximately 2%. It was generally agreed that the percentage of drug use is much higher. In fact, when testing has been carried out without the threat penalties, these positivity rates have been as high as 80%. The positive rate in Belgium is around 8% but a much higher rate would be expected if random testing during training was introduced. In Scandinavia any athlete can be tested during training which apparently controls drug use much more effectively than just competition testing. An analogy was made with the drug of abuse testing in the United States Navy where a 40% positive rate was obtained when random testing was first introduced, but which eventually dropped to 2%.

One real deficiency is the lack of information concerning the extent of the drug problem. One recommended approach would be to interview athletes with absolute guarantees of confidentiality. This approach should lead to reliable data on the true extent of doping in sports.

There was a general agreement on the importance of education of athletes, coaches and the public on the adverse effects that doping is having on both the health of the athlete and the health of the sport. Also it was agreed that too often only the athlete is penalized whereas frequently the real culprit is the coach for having recommended and supplying drugs. The difficulty lies in proving that a coach is involved whereas an identified positive urine specimen certainly incriminates the athlete. For coaches, guilt by association is possible and perhaps the threat of penalties might promote voluntary random testing programs such as those carried out in many United States Universities. Therefore, testing carried out internally weeds out offenders before major intercollegiate events where a positive test results in much publicity and embarrassment to the University involved. This part of the discussion concluded with the agreement that "out of competition" or random testing should be carried out. Presently the IAAF has 170 members only 13 of which conduct testing out of competition.

The discussion then focussed on true analytical aspects. Immunoassays are inadequate at the present time for screening purposes for all types of anabolic steroids. Gas chromatography linked to mass spectrometry (GC/MS) provides the method of choice for screening purposes and also for confirmation. The question was raised if monitoring a single ion is sufficient. The EEC plans to recommend 4 diagnostic ions and 2 internal standards. The relative intensities of these ions must not deviate by more than 5% from the expected intensities.

If the results are equivocal then a new derivative must be prepared and the sample re-analyzed using a different chromatographic column. The problem of the effect of tuning a quadrupole mass spectrometer on relative intensities of ions was discussed. Magnetic sector mass spectrometry provide a more precise measurement of relative ion intensities and perhaps could be used occasionally to check the performance of quadrupole instruments. The use of primary standards is of great help to check relative ion intensities and ensure accurate results. Unfortunately the availability of primary standards is quite limited and virtually non-existent for drug metabolites.

Criteria for confirmation of a positive result were presented using nandrolone as an example. Four diagnostic ions of each of two metabolites was agreed upon. Retention time is an important analytical characteristic and should be within a tolerance of 0.33% or approximately 1 second in 10 minutes. The use of an autosampler is needed to achieve this performance.

Quantitation of drug concentrations poses many questions especially in establishing cut-off values. The limitations of urine as a specimen are considerable. Caffeine was used as an example; some laboratories use 4-5 µg/ml as a cut-off, others as high as 8 µg/ml and the NCAA OEC cutoff is 15 µg/ml. One consideration in establishing a limit is that an athlete might aim to get as close to the limit as possible to provide the maximum advantage.

Quantitation does increase the cost of testing. In the United States in collegiate athletics, cocaine and THC are quantitated. One need is for uniformity in detection limits.

The other considerations in testing are urine pH and specific gravity. Urine pH must be less than 7.5; pH 7.6-8.0 is unacceptable and the athlete and collection crew leader must wait until the urine pH falls to an acceptable level. After hard competition urine pH of around 5.5 is to be expected. Dilute urine specimens pose problems and the use of freeze drying a large volume (50 ml) offers one solution. One paper presented during the conference addressed this aspect (D. Catlin and C. Hatton, Effect of dilution on analysis).

In order to detect testosterone doping, the International Olympic Committee has established a urinary testosterone: epitestosterone ratio of >6 as being evidence of this abuse. There are some non-abusers, however, who normally have a testosterone: epitestosterone ratio >6. The use of T/LH ratio was suggested to provide additional information. Thus, this criterion of testosterone doping should be studied further. Excretion profiles of steroids in all athletes not undergoing doping would be interesting but is not practical at the present time.

Quality assurance was the final point for discussion. Conventional quality assurance programs used in routine clinical chemistry laboratories were presented. Here in-house controls, proficiency test samples and standard reference materials are relied upon to ensure quality. Blind controls that cannot be distinguished from actual samples are an important means of detecting problems. One valuable aspect of proficiency test samples is feedback so that the laboratory can assess performance in relation to peer laboratories. During IOC Accreditation, specimens are submitted to the laboratory for analysis. No feedback is given; however, it was stated that performance is invariably achieved. A final question about a proficiency teat program was the question of finances. Who pays for developing the program which undoubtedly would be quite expensive?

Section 2
Health Effects

Health risks of steroid use

Arne Ljungqvist

Department of Pathology, Karolinska Hospital, Stockholm, Sweden

Abstract - Anabolic-androgenic steroids are widely used by athletes in order to enhance their competitive capacity. The fact that doping is strictly forbidden does not seem to be an effective deterrent. More rational arguments, such as the health risks involved may provide a greater deterrent to anabolic steroid abuse. In the absence of scientific retrospective studies of doped athletes, our knowledge of the health risks of steroid doping is based on occasional reports, second hand information and deduction from prior experience of the use of steroids in human medicine. On the basis of this information, however, it is possible to conclude that the health risks are so severe that from a purely medical standpoint the use of anabolic-androgenic steroids by athletes can not be accepted.

INTRODUCTION

Doping in sport has a long history. In earlier days various drugs or mixtures of drugs were used to stimulate the athlete's competitive capacity at a particular competition. The misuse of such stimulants can be prevented by dope controls at the competitions. This is done by some international sports federations and by the International Olympic Committee at the Olympic Games and other competitions staged under its patronage.

The situation changed drastically in the 1960s when anabolic steroids came into sports. These drugs are taken during the training periods in order to enhance the training effects, particularly muscular growth during strength training. Drugs with similar action (e.g. testosterone, growth hormone and human chorionic gonadotropin) were introduced later into sports. The use of these drugs will only rarely be revealed by dope tests at competitions since most athletes simply stop administering the drug some time before the competition in order to "clear" their urine. Therefore dope testing outside competition would be needed in order to discourage athletes from steroid doping.

Since sports organizations have difficulties in arranging for dope tests outside of competition, the misuse of anabolic steroids and related substances (hereafter referred to as "hormone doping") has escalated and become the greatest problem that competitive sport faces today. Moreover, since drugs are banned, athletes self-administer them secretly in very high dosages and over long periods of time. Not surprisingly, the health risks to these athletes has become of great concern to sports governing bodies. The issue should also be of some concern to society in general since there is a general feeling that hormone doping is widely used not only by senior top athletes but also by athletes at lower levels and at younger ages. This report is an attempt to elucidate the extent of the misuse of drugs in sport and the adverse effects these drugs may have on the athletes with special reference to hormone doping.

STIMULANTS

Besides the fact that doping is strictly forbidden, misuse of stimulants must be discouraged since it will make the athlete increasingly dependent on the drug in order to be able to perform well. The most important substances in this group of drugs are the amphetamines which are known to be highly addictive. The development of true drug addiction, similar to that occurring with chronic heroin abuse, may even result in the death of the individual. Moreover, cases have been recorded of doped athletes who have died during competition (e.g. Olympic Games 1960 and Tour de France some years later). Presumably the stimulants had lead to over exertion and subsequent exhaustion and circulatory collapse. Sports organizations must therefore be encouraged to conduct dope controls at major competitions, not only for the sake of fair competition but also for the protection of the athletes.

Olympic Games are staged every four years (from now on every two years with winter and summer games alternating). At these competitions large numbers of dope tests are taken for analysis. One sample is obtained from each of the first four finalists in each event and from additional athletes chosen at random. This will certainly prevent the misuse of stimulants at Olympic Games. It is important, however, that also the international sports federations conduct dope test at their competitions in order to prevent the misuse of stimulants. An international federation like the International Amateur Athletic Federation (IAAF) does this. The IAAF anti-doping program has developed rapidly over the last five years. Today drug testing takes place both at major games and championships (World Championships, World Cup, continental championships, etc.) and at every major international meeting such as the Grand Prix meetings. In addition, member federations have adopted domestic testing programs which include testing at major and minor national competitions.

STEROIDS

It can be assumed that the misuse of stimulants has gone down considerably, and possibly has been eliminated in track and field athletics due to the extensive drug testing program in that sport. The situation is quite different when it comes to anabolic steroids, testosterone, growth hormone and other substances which are taken during training in order to improve muscle strength and, thus, sports performance. Any anti-doping program which is intended to act as a deterrent must, therefore, include random testing during training. International sports bodies can not be expected to conduct world wide dope testing during training. It must be the responsibility of the different countries in the sporting world to conduct such tests within their domestic anti-doping programs. Unfortunately, very few countries conduct such testing programs. The IAAF probably has the most extensive dope control program of all international sports federations. An investigation carried out in 1986 showed that only 12 of the 174 member federations conducted dope test outside competition and only 31 tested at domestic competitions.

Since anabolic steroids and similar substances are not tested for appropriately, the misuse of these substances has become widespread. The actual extent of this misuse is difficult to assess since the drugs have been banned since 1974 and athletes are reluctant to admit even in anonymous questionnaires that they are cheats (ref. 1). Nor does the frequency of positive cases recorded at laboratory analysis reflect the extent of the misuse, since the samples are mostly collected at competitions.

In Sweden, the national drug testing program has included random testing during training since 1982. In that year, 171 tests were carried out with only 41% of them outside competition. Less than 1% of these tests were confirmed positive. As the testing activity outside competition increased, the frequency of positive cases also increased to reach a peak of 4.4% in 1984. From then on the preventive effect of the testing program became evident and the frequency of positive cases dropped despite an increase in number of tests outside competition. In 1987 a total of 1802 athletes were tested, 85% of them during training. Twenty athletes were found doped, and 13 more refused to give a urine sample. All these 33 athletes (1.8%) were weight lifters, and all the 20 positive samples contained steroids.

That steroids have become the number one doping agent is also supported by recent international statistics. In the years 1985-86 a total of 32 doped athletes were found within the IAAF testing program and 28 of them (87.5%) had taken steroids. The others were positive for ephedrine and related substances. In 1986 a total of 672 positive urine samples were recorded in the accredited doping laboratories around the world and 439 of the (65%) were positive for steroids. Most of the other positive samples contained ephedrine and derivatives thereof. In the experience of the IAAF doping with ephedrine, which is classified within the group of stimulants, is mostly "accidental" resulting from the use of ephedrine-containing over-the-counter cold remedies.

The misuse of hormones is, however, certainly much more extensive than suggested by the incidence recorded at laboratory analysis even though some tests are conducted outside competition. Before anabolic steroids were banned, an investigation was carried out in Sweden on track and field athletes (ref. 2). The top ten in each event were asked if they used steroids and 69% of them replied to the mailed questionnaires. Thirty-one per cent of those who responded admitted the use of anabolic steroids. It is interesting to note that already at that time testosterone was in use. In another study Norgren (ref. 3) sent a questionnaire to all Swedish weight lifters who had represented the country internationally during the period 1970-79. Of the 56 weight lifters approached 47 answered the questionnaire and were further interviewed. Forty-four of these athletes (94%) admitted that they had doped themselves with steroids during their athletic careers. It was also confirmed that athletes take steroids in dosages which are much higher than the maximum therapeutic levels recommended. Thus, they were taking amounts from 50 to 500 mg/week during 4-6 weeks. This medication was repeated 3-4 times/year, up to 10 years in some cases.

Further evidence of the widespread practice of hormone doping was obtained at the Pan American Games in Caracas 1983. The drug testing which took place there was unannounced to the athletes. When it became known that some power athletes were found positive during the early stages of the games many athletes left Caracas without participating thus creating a great scandal, particularly in the USA. It is reasonable to assume that the athletes left because they believed that they may might be found guilty at a dope test.

In 1987 BBC televised a documentary report in which the international trafficking of doping substances, particularly anabolic-androgenic steroids, was revealed. It mimics to a great extent the illegal trade of narcotic drugs with eager consumers at the end of the chain. The large sums of money that were found to be involved suggest a large consumption of the doping agents. In many countries, but not all, anabolic steroids can only be obtained through doctor's prescription. Initially anabolic steroids seemed to be a promising group of drugs for treatment of various conditions but today the prescription rate of the drugs is extremely low in a country such as Sweden. The easy availability of steroids in sport can only be explained by an illegal influx of the drugs into the country, again indicating an organized and significant international trafficking of the drugs, and self-medication amongst athletes.

It can be deduced from direct and indirect evidence that hormone doping is widespread in sport, particularly in those sports where muscle strength is of importance. Therefore, the health risks to the athletes who take such drugs must be the concern not only of the sports organizations but of society in general. The adverse effects of hormone doping are of short term and long term character. The short term effects are best known and many of them can be verified only by various laboratory tests. The long term effects are largely unknown. Experience from human medical practice can only give vague information due to the considerable dosage differences. Moreover, no follow up study of a population of earlier hormone doped athletes has been reported. Our suspicions of possibly serious long term effects are therefore based on the assumption that chronic end stages of originally short term organ damage may develop after prolonged misuse of the drugs. The known adverse effects of doping with steroids fall into one of two categories: endocrinological effects and toxic effects.

Endocrinological effects
These effects vary with age. In adult men the plasma testosterone and gonad-otropin levels decrease as does the spermiogenesis (refs. 4,5). In athletes who were self-administering large dosages of anabolic-androgenic steroids Alén and Häkkinen (ref. 6) found a prolonged depression of spermiogenesis with azooapermia. The danger of an irreversible testicular atrophy and sterility in prolonged or repeated heavy hormone misuse is therefore obvious. The use of anabolic steroids also depresses the plasma levels of luteinizing hormone (LH) and follicle stimulating hormone (FSH). The exact mechanism by which the steroids cause these effects on the hormones and spermiogenesis is not known but two possible mechanisms have been proposed. Either the steroid replaces testosterone in a negative feed back system which leads to a decreased production of gonadotropins and hence testosterone, or possibly anabolic steroids compete with endogenous testosterone for protein-binding sites on testosterone-binding globulin (ref. 7).

In women the prolonged use of anabolic steroids and related substances leads to virilization which includes lowering of the voice due to changes in the larynx and the vocal cords, increase facial and body hair, enlarged clitoris and decreased breast size. Changes in, or absence of, menstrual function and loss of scalp hair has also been reported in women athletes taking anabolic steroids (ref. 8). It is worth mentioning that the masculinization in women is an irreversible change.

Other endocrine reactions are the occurrence of acne, altered glucose tolerance and hyperinsulinism in both men and women, and gynecomastia in men (ref. 7). In the growing boys and girls, the use of anabolic steroids may lead to premature closure of the epiphyseal growth zones resulting in an early cessation of growth (ref. 9).

In recent years a decrease in the plasma level of high density lipoprotein (HDL) has been reported in athletes taking anabolic steroids (refs. 10,11). HDL is of importance in the transport of cholesterol from the tissues to the liver for catabolism (ref. 12). Therefore HDL-cholesterol is regarded as a "good" cholesterol which may protect the individual from developing atherosclerosis and cardiovascular disease. During intense training and exercise HDL is usually elevated (ref. 13) and physical activity is therefore regarded as possibly protective against the development of atherosclerosis and cardiovascular disease. Since anabolic steroids act in the opposite way it can be assumed that athletes misusing these drugs run a greater cardiovascular risk. It should be emphasized, however, that the importance of HDL in ischemic heart disease is questionable (ref. 14). In this connection it is, however, of some interest to note that in a review of sudden deaths in competitive athletes 3 out of 29 could be attributed to coronary atherosclerosis (ref. 15).

Although the anabolic steroids were originally produced with the aim to exercise an anabolic effect like testosterone, but not the androgenic effect of that hormone, a complete elimination of the androgenic properties could not be achieved. It is therefore not surprising that athletes develop androgenic effects when they take the drugs in very high dosages. The above mentioned virilization of women is one such effect. Other androgenic effects observed in athletes are often referred to as "behavioral effects" and include increased aggressiveness and sometimes euphoria and diminished fatigue. It may, in fact, be these effects rather than any anabolic effects that make the athlete benefit from anabolic steroids; he simply can train more often and more intensely. In the study by Ljungqvist (ref. 2) such behavioral effects increased aggressiveness and training capacity whereas others reported increased fatigue, sleeping problems, mood swings and occasionally light confusion.

In Sweden, we have recorded several cases in which athletes who were on high dosages of anabolic steroids experienced severe confusion and aggression after alcohol consumption. In two of these cases, in which the alcohol consumption was low or moderate, the athletes became severely confused and aggressive beyond their own control and committed criminal acts, one of which ended in homicide. Whether the taking of anabolic steroids was important in these incidents can, of course, not be fully assessed. There is a general experience that the adverse effects on the behavior disappear after the discontinuation of the drug (ref. 16).

Toxic effects
The toxic effects reported in steroid users are mostly related to damage of the liver. Thus, peliosis hepatis, hepatic cholestasis and increased transaminase levels in the blood have been reported (refs. 16,17). Peliosis hepatis is a peculiar angiomatous lesion of the liver and mostly an accidental finding, but it may be fatal (ref. 18). Elevation of serum transaminases and hepatic cholestasis are both reversible after discontinuation of the drug. Their occurrence suggests, however, that prolonged or repeated heavy use of steroids may ultimately lead to severe and chronic liver damage. Even more serious is, however, the possible development of malignant liver tumor (ref. 19).

In the experimental animal, damage has been reported in the myofibrills and mitochondria of cardiac tissue after anabolic steroid administration (refs. 20,21,22). In particular, the combination of physical exercise and administration of steroids proved harmful to the myocardial cells (ref. 20). It is not clear to what extent such damage may occur in athletes. The combined risk of atherosclerotic cardiac disease resulting from lowered HDL cholesterol and the direct toxic effects on the cardiac tissue are facts that should be taken into account in future follow up studies of the cardiovascular system of hormone doped athletes.

Finally, it should be remembered that some hormone doping includes injections of the drugs. They are carried out secretly and without the help of medical expertise. The risk of imperfect needle and syringe sterility and consequent transmission of type B hepatis and HIV-infection is therefore obvious (ref. 23).

In conclusion, hormone doping causes such striking biological changes in the body that the possibility of severe long term organ damage must be taken into account. Moreover, hormone doping contravenes basic ethical principles of fair and sound competitions. Hormone doping has therefore been condemned by responsible sports medical bodies like the American College of Sports Medicine (ref. 24). The panel of scandinavian medical experts, assembled in 1985 on the initiative of the swedish anti-doping commission in Stockholm, issued the following statement: "The panel unanimously established the fact that earlier studies in different parts of the world, as well as more recent studies carried out by Prof. Alén in Jyvaskylä, have demonstrated such biological effects of anabolic-androgenic steroids on athletes that the possibility of permanent lesions from long term misuse of these drugs can not be ruled out. The medical reasons for not using the drugs as doping agents are therefore further strengthened."

REFERENCES

1. A. Ljungqvist, Scand. J. Sports. Sci. 8, 51-55 (1986).
2. A. Ljungqvist, Brit. J. Sports Med. 9, 82 (1975).
3. P. Norgren, Doping i Svensk Tyngdlyftning pp. 1-35, HLSTryck (1984).
4. S.B. Stromme, H.D. Meen and A. Aakvaag, Med. Sci. Sprts Exerc. 6, 203-208 (1974).
5. A. Clerico, M. Ferdeghini, C. Palombo et Al., J. Nucl. Med. Allied Sci. 25, 79-88 (1981).
6. M. Alén and K. Häkkinen, Int. J. Sports Med. 6, 24-29 (1985).
7. M.W. Kibble and M.B. Ross, Clin. Pharm. 6, 686-692 (1987).
8. R.H. Strauss, M.T. Liggett and R.R. Lanese, JAMA 253, 2873 (1985).
9. M.J. Whitelaw, T.N. Foster and W.H. Graham, Pediatric. Pharm. Ther. 68, 291-296 (1966).
10. M. Alén and P. Rahkila, Int. J. Sports Med. 5, 341-344 (1984).
11. O.L. Webb, E.M. Laskarzewski and C.J. Glueck, Metabolism 33, 971-975 (1984).
12. A. Gotto, E.L. Bierman, W.E. Connor et al., Circulation 69, 1065-1090 (1984).
13. S.C. Enger, K. Herbjorensen, J. Erikssen et al., Scan. J. Clin. Invest. 137, 251-255 (1977).
14. S.J. Pocock, A.G. Shaper, A.N. Phillips, M. Walker and T.P. Whitehead, Brit. Med. J. 292, 515-519 (1986).
15. B.J. Maron, W.C. Roberts, H.A. McAllister et al. Circulation 62, 218-229 (1980).
16. B.S. Gordon, J. Walf, T. Krause and F. Shai, Amer. J. Clin. Path. 33, 156-165 (1960).
17. H.A. Haupt and G.D. Rovere, Am. J. Sports Med. 12, 469-484 (1984).
18. S. Sherlock, Diseases of the liver and biliary system, pp 561-562, Blackwell Sci. Publ., Oxford London Edinburgh Melbourne, 5th ed. (1975).
19. W.L. Overly, J.A. Dankoff, B.K. Wang et al. Ann. Intern. Med. 100, 158-159 (1984).
20. H.J. Appell, B. Heller-Umpfenbach, M. Feraudi and H. Weicer, Int. J. Sports Med. 4, 268-274 (1983).
21. H. Behrendt and H. Boffin, Cell Tissue Res. 181, 423-426 (1977).
22. H. Behrendt, Cell Tissue Res. 180, 305-315 (1977).
23. H.M. Sklarek, R.P. Mantovani, E. Erens et al., N. Engl. J. Med. 311, 1701 (1984).
24. Amer. Coll. Sports Med. Sports Med. Bull. 19, 13-18 (1984).

Potential role of synthetic sex steroids in hepatocarcinogenesis

Stan D. Vesselinovitch, N. Mihailovich, and K.V.N. Rao

Departments of Pathology and Radiology, University of Chicago, Chicago, Ill.

Abstract – The endogenous sex steroid hormones modify the development of
tumors not only in the physiologically targeted organs (mammary glands,
ovaries, and testes) but also at other organ sites (liver and kidney).
The endogenous androgens accelerate and the estrogens delay the development of experimentally hepatocellular tumors induced in the laboratory
animals. The epidemiological studies indicated an association of liver
tumors with the use of oral contraceptives in women and anabolic androgenic
steroids in men. The extensive and long-term studies from our laboratory
demonstrated the modifying effect of endogenous and exogenous steroid hormones upon the chemically-induced hepatocarcinogenesis. In the first
series of studies, the host hormonal environment was changed by gonadectomy following single initiating treatment of infant mice with diethylnitrosamine (DEN). Data showed that endogenous androgens accelerated and
the estrogens delayed the development of non-neoplastic and neoplastic
hepatocellular nodular lesions. In the second series, the hormonally intact infant mice were treated with DEN and subsequently were administered
oral contraceptives (mestranol and/or norethynodrel) to females and anabolic androgen steroids (methyltestosterone and/or oxymetholone) to males.
The synthetic steroid treatments influenced the emergence of tinctorial
foci and nodular non-neoplastic and neoplastic lesions in the liver due
to their modifying effect upon the host's hormonal environment. The administration of mestranol and/or norethynodrel to females changed the
endogenous hormonal environment similar to that following ovariectomy.
Consequently, the development of focal and nodular liver lesions was
accelerated. The administration of methyltestosterone and oxymetholone
to males changed the internal hormonal environment similar to that following orchidectomy. Therefore, the development of focal and nodular liver
lesions induced by DEN was delayed. In contrast, the chronic administration of any of the above synthetic steroids to the animals, which were
not pretreated with a hepatocarcinogen, did not influence the development
of spontaneously occurring nodular liver lesions. It is apparent, therefore, that synthetic steroids could be considered only as modulators of
induced hepatocarcinogenesis and not as inducers of liver tumor development per se. Assuming that a similar mode of action is applicable to
humans, the use of synthetic steroids could represent a significant carcinogenic risk only to individuals exposed to chemical or viral liver
carcinogens. Since other predisposing conditions like hepatitis B virus
infection may play an important role in the development of hepatocellular
carcinomas, athletes and other users of the steroid hormones may be
screened for the viral infection before the administration of the agents.

INTRODUCTION

Primary hepatocellular carcinoma, although a relatively rare disease in the Western countries, is probably the most common cancer in certain regions like the Far East and Sub-
Saharan Africa (ref. 1). Irrespective of the wide geographic variation in the incidence,
it is predominantly manifested in males, the male to female ratio being as high as 4:1 or
more. Despite its rarity in the Western countries, during the past two decades, there has
been an increasing concern over the occurrence of benign and malignant tumors, particularly of the liver, in users of oral contraceptive pills and androgenic-anabolic steroid
hormones (refs. 2 and 3). Both groups of the agents have common structural features and
produced similar non-neoplastic and neoplastic lesions in the liver (ref. 4). In 1972, the

British Committee on Safety of Medicine concluded that oral contraceptive steroids were apparently devoid of hepatocarcinogenic activity (ref. 5). Even after extensive investigations (ref. 6), controversy still exists as to the carcinogenic potential of oral contraceptives. However, recent case-controlled studies in Britain by Neuberger et al. (ref. 7) and Forman et al. (ref. 8) indicated a low but significant increased risk for women taking the pill for 8 or more years. On the other hand, except for isolated reports, no such data are available in regard to the androgenic-anabolic steroids (ref. 3), partly because the illicit users like athletes tend to be secretive (refs. 9 and 10). Also, in contrast to oral contraceptives, the androgenic-anabolic steroids are used by the heterogenous population, including athletes and body-builders of both sexes, patients with anemic conditions and hypogonadism (refs. 3 and 10), as well as by transsexuals (refs. 11 and 12). Besides the liver, tumor development in other hormone-sensitive extrahepatic tissues like the prostate (ref. 13), colon (ref. 14), and kidney (ref. 15) have been reported but their causal relationship to the use of the androgenic-anabolic steroids is uncertain. However, in view of the large doses in which these agents are taken orally and parenterally and the general propensity of androgens and compounds having anabolic properties to enhance hepatocarcinogenesis in laboratory animals, considerable risk may be anticipated for the exposed individuals. As representative agents, we have investigated the carcinogenic potential of methyltestosterone and oxymetholone, which are anabolic steroids frequently associated with liver tumors in case reports, in the infant mouse hepatocarcinogenesis model developed in our laboratory. Similar studies were conducted with combinations of norethynodrel and mestranol, the agents widely used for oral contraception. Since these compounds and steroid hormones in general lacked mutagenic and hepatogenotoxic activities (ref. 16), the promoting effects of all of the selected hormones were assessed using appropriate protocols. In addition, the modulating effects of alteration in natural hormonal environment on spontaneous and induced hepatocarcinogenesis in this model are also presented here for comparison.

Our interest in this field stems from a series of integrated studies regarding the role of endogenous sex steroid hormones in hepatocarcinogenesis using an experimental animal model developed in our laboratories. This model explored the carcinogenic process triggered by a single administration of diethylnitrosamine (DEN) to infant mice. Such treatment resulted in the sequential development of hepatocellular basophilic foci, hepatocellular nodules, hepatocellular adenomas, and hepatocellular carcinomas. The rate of hepatocarcinogenesis was dependent, however, upon the hormonal environment of the host. Thus, although both male and female mice showed the same DEN dealkylation (ref. 17), similar DNA ethylation (ref. 18) and similar quantitative response, the temporal relationship of hepatocarcinogenesis was dependent upon the sex hormonal environment of the host; the liver tumors developed sooner in the males than in the females. The change in the hormonal environment by orchidectomy and ovariectomy or the administration of the synthetic oral contraceptives and anabolic steroids influenced the rate of tumor development rather than their incidence in males and females.

The objective of this paper is three-fold: (a) to outline the carcinogenic process and the two-stage operational approach to carcinogenesis, (b) to summarize data regarding neoplastic effects of anabolic steroids in humans and sex steroids in experimental animals, and (c) to present some experimental data from our laboratory regarding the role of endogenous sex hormones, methyltestosterone, oxymetholone, mestranol, and norethynodrel in hepatocarcinogenesis.

CARCINOGENIC PROCESS AND THE TWO-STAGE CONCEPT OF CARCINOGENESIS

Table 1 presents an overview of the steps which take place from the administration of a carcinogen (most likely a procarcinogen) through its activation and interaction with the intranuclear macromolecular site(s), formation of the initiated cells, and the occurrence of the additional events resulting in the neoplastic, actively dividing cells. Operationally the carcinogenic process can be divided into two stages: initiation and promotion. Complete carcinogens possess both the initiating and promoting activities. Some agents, however, could be only initiators and promoters. Complete carcinogenesis represents a greater health risk than do the initiators and promoters, respectively.

In order to clarify the promoting role of endogenous and synthetic steroids more comprehensible, it is necessary to outline the so-called initiation-promotion concept of carcinogenesis. This concept was developed originally by Friedenwald and Rous (ref. 19) and expanded later by Berenblum and Shubik (refs. 20 and 21). These concepts were applied originally to the elucidation of skin carcinogenesis and more recently to the process of liver carcinogenesis. The principle is as follows: some agents may on their own induce neoplasia in target tissue(s), while the others could either begin ("initiate") or terminate ("promote") the neoplastic process. Under the latter assumption, the low doses of complete carcinogens or the agents which are only initiators can begin but not terminate the process. The completion of the process can be achieved by agents lacking the initiating carcinogenic activity but possessing the promoting or developing carcinogenic action. Promoting agents are active only when applied following but not when administered before the administration of an initiating treatment.

TABLE 1. Outline of the carcinogenic process

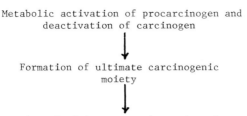

Metabolic activation of procarcinogen and
deactivation of carcinogen

↓

Formation of ultimate carcinogenic
moiety

↓

Interaction of ultimate carcinogenic moiety with
critical macromolecular site(s) leading to
the formation of primary macromolecular
lesion(s)

↓

Fixation/repair of the primary lesion resulting in
the residual macromolecular lesion(s) which
represents the primary carcinogenic event
transforming affected hepatocytes into
initiated (potentially neoplastic)
cells

↓

Subsequent carcinogenic events (temporal cascade of
gene's activation) which occur as a result of the
unfolding of the initial genetic program
or as a response to the additional
"promoting" stimuli

The outline presented in Table 2 will clarify the above operational concept. Thus, one has
to consider two sequential types of treatment: initiation and promotion. The initiating
treatment is usually single while the promoting treatment has to be given repeatedly for an
extended period of time. The proper sequence of those treatments (initiation followed by
promotion) is essential for tumor development. The administration of initiator or promoter
alone is ineffective in inducing tumor development (sequences 1 and 2). The initiator-
promoter sequence results in tumor development (sequence 3). The reversal of treatments is
ineffective for tumor induction (sequence 4). This model does not give any explanation of
the underlying mechanism for each action. Nevertheless, the initiation is considered as
representing genetic change. The promotion is considered as being paragenetic in nature
and operating only by facilitating the occurrence of the additional events necessary for
the expression of neoplasia

TABLE 2. Outline of the initiation-promotion concept of carcinogenesis

Sequence	1st Treatment	2nd Treatment	Tumor response
1	Initiator	None	None
2	None	Promoter	None
3	Initiator	Promoter	Present
4	Promoter	Initiator	None

NEOPLASTIC EFFECTS OF ANABOLIC STEROIDS IN HUMANS AND SEX STEROIDS IN EXPERIMENTAL ANIMALS

The compilation of the case reports indicated a contributory role of anabolic androgenic
steroids to hepatocarcinogenesis and the development of colon and prostate carcinomas
(Table 3). These observations were backed up by a series of laboratory investigations
which showed that high dose levels of these agents (100-fold of dosages given to humans)
were weakly "hepatocarcinogenic" to mice, rats, and hamsters, in ascending order of response (ref. 22). In addition, specifically designed studies pointed out that synthetic
steroids may act as promoters of hepatocarcinogenesis and as the inducers of prostate
gland carcinogenesis (Table 4).

TABLE 3. Neoplastic effects of anabolic steroids in man - case reports

Treatment	Reasons for taking steroids	Neoplasia or disease	Reference
Testosterone enanthate, nandrolone decanoate, oxymetholone	Hemodialysis for chronic renal failure leading to anemia (9)[a]	Three cases of intra-hepatic tumors: cholangiocarcinoma, cholangiocellular and hepatocellular carcinoma, hepato-cellular carcinoma	Turani et al. (ref. 23)
Various anabolic steroids	Aplastic anemia (19)	Seven cases of peliosis hepatitis	Wakabayashi et al. (ref. 24)
Various anabolic steroids	Fanconi's anemia (14) Aplastic anemia (10) Other conditions (12)	Hepatocellular ade-noma Hepatic angiosarcoma Intrahepatic cholan-giocarcinoma Hepatic adenoma Benign hyperplasia	Haupt and Rovere (ref. 3)
Anabolic steroids for 4 years, needles were often shared	Body-builder (1)	AIDS at 37 years of age	Sklarek et al. (ref. 25)
Methenolone enanthate oxandrolone for 8 years	Body-builder (1)	Colorectal carcinoma at 27 years of age	Edis and Levitt (ref. 14)
Various anabolic androgens including defadurabolin for 18 years	Body-builder (1)	Adenocarcinoma of the prostate at 38 years of age	Roberts and Essenhigh (ref. 13)

[a]Number of cases in parentheses.

THE ROLE OF SEX HORMONAL ENVIRONMENT UPON INDUCED HEPATOCARCINOGENESIS

Considering the above concept, a series of integrated studies were carried out in which the host's hormonal environment was influenced by gonadectomy or by the administration of syn-thetic steroids. Also, synthetic steroids were tested for their full carcinogenic poten-tial. It should be emphasized, however, that in the former studies the effect of the test agents was investigated as to their effects upon the ongoing carcinogenic process triggered by DEN rather than upon the solely initiated cells.

The effect of gonadectomy upon hepatocarcinogenesis induced by DEN
Table 5 shows that the reduction of endogenous androgen following orchidectomy reduced and delayed the emergence of hepatocellular adenomas and carcinomas induced by single doses of DEN (1.25 to 5.0 μg/g body weight). Thus, one can conclude that the presence of endogenous testosterone in the non-orchidectomized males accelerated and enhanced the development of focal and nodular liver lesions. It also enhanced the progression of hepatocarcinogenesis. The ovariectomy of the DEN-treated females accelerated the development of the same type of lesions (ref. 26). Thus the presence of the endogenous estrogens in the non-ovariectomized females delayed the emergence and the progression of hepatocarcinogenesis. It is obvious, therefore, that the androgen/estrogen ratio of the host can modulate the rate of the time-dependent events of hepatocarcinogenesis.

TABLE 4. Effect of sex steroids on carcinogenesis in experimental animals

Treatment		Response	Reference
1st	2nd		
Hepatocarcinogenesis			
N-nitrosomorpholine, ovariectomized rats	Estradiol phenyl-propionate or estradiol benzoate	Enhanced hepato-carcinogenesis	Taper (ref. 27)
Diethylnitrosamine, Sprague-Dawley female rats	Mestranol and/or norethynodrel	Enhanced appearance of tinctorial foci	Yager and Yager (ref. 28)
Diethylnitrosamine, Fischer 344 male rats	Ethinylestradiol	Enhanced appearance of precancerous lesions	Cameron et al. (ref. 29)
Ethinylestradiol or diethylstilbestrol, Fischer 344 male rats	None	Enhanced appearance of tinctorial foci and hyperplastic nodules	Wanless and Medline (ref. 30)
Diethylnitrosamine, B6C3F$_1$ female mice	Mestranol	Enhanced incidence and multiplicity of hepatocellular adenomas	Vesselinovitch and Mihailovich (ref.31)
Diethylnitrosamine, Sprague-Dawley rats	Mestranol or ethinyl-estradiol	Increase in hepato-cellular nodules and carcinomas	Yager et al. (ref. 32)
Methyltestosterone, BALB/c mice	None	Induction of hepatocellular nodules	Taylor et al. (ref. 33)
Diethylnitrosamine, BALB/c male mice	Decadurabolin, s.c. for 6 weeks	Enhancement of liver tumors	Lesna and Taylor (ref. 34)
Prostate carcinogenesis			
Testosterone propio-nate, NB male rats	None	Induction of adeno-carcinoma in the prostate gland	Noble (refs. 35,36)
N-nitrosobis (2-oxopropyl) amine (BOP)	Testosterone propio-nate before and/or after BOP, Wistar-derived MRC rats	Modified initiation and promotion of prostatic carci-noma	Pour and Stepan (ref. 37)
Methylnitroso-urea (MNU)	Testosterone propio-nate, Lobund-Wistar rats	Enhancement of development of prostatic adeno-carcinoma	Pollard and Luckert (ref. 38)

TABLE 5.   Effect of orchidectomy upon hepatocarcinogenesis[a]

Orchi-dectomy[c]	Response at weeks	μg of DEN/g body weight[b]					
		1.25		2.5		5.0	
		Ade-noma	Carci-noma	Ade-noma	Carci-noma	Ade-noma	Carci-noma
No	36	9.2	0.0	27.5	0.0	44.3	0.0
Yes		0.0	0.0	0.0	0.0	1.9	0.0
No	44	24.7	0.1	59.7	1.3	130.2	0.4
Yes		0.0	0.0	4.4	0.0	7.8	0.0
No	52	39.7	1.2	32.5	1.1	126.2	8.0
Yes		3.8	0.0	7.9	0.3	16.4	0.5
No	68	63.2	9.2	99.2	13.4	ND[d]	ND
Yes		10.3	0.3	46.2	2.1		

[a] The body of the table gives the average numbers of hepatocellular adenomas and carcinomas in hormonally-intact (sham-orchidectomy) and orchidectomized males.
[b] DEN was injected once intraperitoneally into 15-day-old $B6C3F_1$ male mice.
[c] Orchidectomy was carried out at 4 weeks of age.
[d] ND = not done.

The effect of synthetic anabolic and estrogenic steroids on spontaneous hepatocarcinogenesis

Tables 6 and 7 present the results of studies in which animals were exposed only to synthetic steroids in food. Male animals (Table 6) were exposed to low dose levels of methyltestosterone (6 and 60 ppm) and oxymetholone (12 and 120 ppm) for a period of 56 weeks, starting at 6 weeks of age. The female animals (Table 7) were exposed to low dose levels of mestranol (0.003 and 0.015 ppm) and/or norethynodrel (0.2 and 1.0 ppm) for periods of 70 weeks, beginning at 6 weeks of age. Animals were killed at 62 and 76 weeks for males and females, respectively. The livers were examined histologically for the presence of various non-neoplastic and neoplastic lesions, the images of which were quantitated stereomorphometrically. The data showed that the treatment with any of the above steroids alone did not enhance statistically the spontaneous development of focal or nodular liver lesions in either sex. This indicated an absence of carcinogenic effect of the evaluated synthetic steroids under specified experimental conditions.

Modulating effect of synthetic steroids on DEN-induced hepatocarcinogenesis

In order to test the modulating effect of synthetic steroids on DEN-induced hepatocarcinogenesis, methyltestosterone, oxymetholone, mestranol, and norethynodrel were fed at the same dose levels and duration of time as above to animals which were administered either 0.3 or 0.6 μg of DEN/g body weight intraperitoneally at 15 days of age. Both the low and high DEN dose level treated animals were administered low and high dose levels of synthetic steroids.

Studies in males. The administration of methyltestosterone and oxymetholone to male mice which were conditioned by 0.3 μg of DEN/g body weight had a tendency to lower the average number and the total weight of hepatocellular adenomas per liver. Similar effects of methyltestosterone and oxymetholone were seen in animals which were conditioned by 0.6 μg of DEN/g but were exposed subsequently to the low level of these two anabolic androgens (6 ppm and 12 ppm, respectively). In contrast, when the higher dosages of methyltestosterone (60 ppm) and/or oxymetholone (120 ppm) were administered following 0.6 μg of DEN treatment, no inhibitory effect upon hepatocarcinogenesis was observed. Actually, the oxymetholone treated showed an apparent increase in the average number of foci and hepatocellular nodules. Thus it may be assumed that an additional increase in the dose of the anabolic steroids could have further enhanced the number of hepatocellular foci and

nodular lesions. This assumption is further substantiated by the studies from other laboratories in which substantially higher dosages (100-fold) of synthetic steroids were hepatocarcinogenic (ref. 22).

TABLE 6. Potential hepatocarcinogenicity of methyltestosterone and oxymetholone
in B6C3F$_1$ male mice

Treatment[a]	Average number of lesions/liver				
	All types of lesions	Types of hepatocellular lesions			
		Foci	Nodules	Adenomas	Carcinomas
None	0.4	0.0	0.0	0.4	0.0
6 ppm methyltestosterone	0.3	0.0	0.0	0.3	0.0
60 ppm methyltestosterone	0.6	0.0	0.0	0.6	0.0
12 ppm oxymetholone	7.1	6.6	0.5	0.0	0.0
120 ppm oxymetholone	1.1	0.8	0.0	0.3	0.0

[a]Methyltestosterone and oxymetholone were administered in food for 56 weeks beginning at 6 weeks of age. Experiment was terminated at 62 weeks of age.

TABLE 7. Potential hepatocarcinogenesis of mestranol and/or norethynodrel in
B6C3F$_1$ female mice

Treatment[a]	Average number of lesions/liver				
	All types of lesions	Types of hepatocellular lesions			
		Foci	Nodules	Adenomas	Carcinomas
None	0.0	0.0	0.0	0.0	0.0
0.003 ppm mestranol	0.0	0.0	0.0	0.0	0.0
0.015 ppm mestranol	0.0	0.0	0.0	0.0	0.0
0.200 ppm norethynodrel	0.0	0.0	0.0	0.0	0.0
1.000 ppm norethynodrel	0.0	0.0	0.0	0.0	0.0
0.003 ppm mestranol + 0.200 ppm norethynodrel	0.0	0.0	0.0	0.0	0.0
0.015 ppm mestranol + 1.000 ppm norethynodrel	0.0	0.0	0.0	0.0	0.0

[a]Mestranol and/or norethynodrel were administered in food for 70 weeks beginning
at 6 weeks of age. Experiment was terminated at 76 weeks of age.

Studies in females. The effect of mestranol and/or norethynodrel upon induced hepatocarcinogenesis was dependent upon the dose of DEN (0.3 or 0.6 µg of DEN/g body weight) and
the dose levels of synthetic steroids. Thus, the low dose of mestranol (0.003 ppm) enhanced
statistically the average number of tinctorial foci in animals pretreated with 0.3 µg of
DEN. However, when a 5-fold higher dose level of mestranol (0.015 ppm) was used under the
identical DEN treatment, no enhancing effect of mestranol upon hepatocarcinogenesis was observed. In contrast, norethynodrel alone or in combination with mestranol failed to enhance
hepatocarcinogenesis.

In the high dose series (0.6 µg of DEN/g body weight), the low dose of mestranol (0.003 ppm)
showed an enhancement of the average number of all types of hepatocellular lesions and the
average numbers of tinctorial foci and hepatocellular adenomas. A low dose of norethynodrel
(0.2 ppm) enhanced the average number of all types of hepatocellular lesions and the average

number of tinctorial foci. The combined treatments of low doses of mestranol and norethynodrel enhanced the average number of all types of hepatocellular lesions and the average number of tinctorial foci (Table 8). The high dose levels of mestranol (0.015 ppm) and
norethynodrel (1.0 ppm) increased the average number of all types of lesions, the hepatocellular foci and the hepatocellular nodules. The combined treatments of high doses of
mestranol and norethynodrel had no effect upon hepatocarcinogenesis (Table 9).

TABLE 8. Effect of mestranol and/or norethynodrel on hepatocarcinogenesis induced by 0.6 µg of DEN/g body weight in 15-day-old B6C3F$_1$ female mice

Treatment		Average number of lesions/liver				
			Types of hepatocellular lesions			
1st[a]	2nd[b]	All types of lesions	Foci	Nodules	Ade-nomas	Carci-nomas
DEN	None	14.6	6.1	4.0	4.3	0.2
DEN	0.003 ppm mestranol	27.8↑	14.1	5.1	8.3↑	0.3
DEN	0.200 ppm norethynodrel	35.8↑	21.3↑	7.8	6.6	0.1
DEN	0.003 ppm mestranol + 0.200 ppm norethynodrel	26.2↑	16.8↑	4.1	5.1	0.2

[a]DEN = diethylnitrosamine
[b]Mestranol and/or norethynodrel were administered during secondary treatment
in food for 70 weeks beginning at 6 weeks of age. Experiment was terminated
at 76 weeks of age. The arrow (↑) indicates an increase in the number of
lesions per liver in orchidectomized vs. non-orchidectomized animals.

TABLE 9. Effect of mestranol and/or norethynodrel on hepatocarcinogenesis induced by 0.6 µg of DEN/g body weight in 15-day-old B6C3F$_1$ female mice

Treatment		Average number of lesions/liver				
			Types of hepatocellular lesions			
1st[a]	2nd[b]	All types of lesions	Foci	Nodules	Ade-nomas	Carci-nomas
DEN	None	14.6	6.1	4.0	4.3	0.2
DEN	0.015 ppm mestranol	29.5↑	13.9↑	7.8	7.5	0.3
DEN	1.000 ppm norethynodrel	34.0↑	16.1↑	13.3↑	4.3	0.3
DEN	0.015 ppm mestranol + 1.000 ppm norethynodrel	19.4	8.5	3.9	6.3	0.7

[a]DEN = diethylnitrosamine.
[b]Mestranol and/or norethynodrel were administered during secondary treatment
in food for 70 weeks beginning at 6 weeks of age. Experiment was terminated
at 76 weeks of age. The arrow (↑) indicates an increase in the number of
lesions per liver in orchidectomized and non-orchidectomized animals.

Thus, under specific experimental conditions, both mestranol and norethynodrel enhanced
hepatocarcinogenesis induced by DEN. Norethynodrel was less effective in enhancing hepatocarcinogenesis than mestranol. The combined administration of low dose levels of mestranol
and norethynodrel enhanced DEN induced hepatocarcinogenesis.

DISCUSSION

The accumulated case reports suggest that hormonal oral contraceptives might be causally related to the development of hepatocellular tumors in women (ref. 6). Experimental laboratory studies support this claim, indicating an enhancing or promoting effect in hepatocarcinogenesis rather than the inducing or initiating carcinogenic potential of oral contraceptives (ref. 22). According to the studies of Schulte-Hermann et al. (ref. 39), some of the synthetic steroids could operate as promoting agents due to their mitogenic, hormonal, and/or enzyme-inducing capacities.

In the case of anabolic androgens, the incriminating evidence is less evident. It is based on isolated case reports suggesting a causal relationship between the use of anabolic androgens and the development of the primary liver tumors. However, it is important to note that the use of anabolic androgens was not restricted to a homogeneous group of healthy individuals. The majority of individuals received hormonal treatment because of their illness, were recipients of blood transfusions, or were undergoing blood dialysis. Therefore, it is not known whether those conditions rather than the administration of anabolic steroids were causally related to the development of liver tumors. This raises the question if the anabolic androgens as such could be involved in hepatocarcinogenesis in healthy individuals. More recently there are indications that the administration of anabolic steroids was causally related not only to the development of liver tumors (ref. 22) but also to the development of tumors in other hormone-sensitive organs, e.g., prostatic adenocarcinoma (ref. 13), colonic adenocarcinoma (ref. 14), and Wilms' tumor (ref. 15). The limited number of those cases does not permit a definite conclusion.

The experimental studies are also inconclusive. A study reported by Lesna and Taylor (ref. 34) showed that the administration of decadurabolin after DEN enhanced the development of liver tumors in male BALB/c mice. The use of single and much lower dose levels of DEN, in conjunction with the protracted oral administration of methyltestosterone and oxymetholone, did not lead to enhanced hepatocarcinogenesis. In fact, methyltestosterone and oxymetholone showed an inhibition of the development of DEN-induced liver tumors. Nevertheless, when oxymetholone was administered following 0.6 μg of DEN/g body weight, there was a slightly enhanced hepatocarcinogenesis. It is possible that higher dosages of oxymetholone and even methyltestosterone could enhance hepatocarcinogenesis if they were administered following exposure to higher dosages of DEN. Previous studies by Taylor et al. (ref. 33) showed that the oral administration of methyltestosterone to BALB/c mice was weakly hepatocarcinogenic.

The data presented herein demonstrated the profound influence of gonadal hormones on hepatocarcinogenesis consistent with the observations in humans and in other animals such as the rat (ref. 40). The effect of synthetic steroids on hepatocarcinogenesis was dependent upon the degree of tumor induction by DEN as well as upon the dose levels at which the compounds were administered. This may explain the opposing reports by different authors (ref. 22) and emphasizes that the dose levels of these agents can operate differentially, depending upon their potential for interference with the endogenous hormonal environment. Androgenic anabolic steroids altered the hormonal homeostasis in healthy men, being particularly effective in suppressing the endogenous production of testosterone (ref. 41). Many other factors and experimental conditions, such as species variation, sex and age of the animal, gonadectomy and partial hepatectomy preceding the administration of the steroids, might have been responsible for the differential responses. Also, the species-specific metabolism of the agents and the incidence of spontaneous tumors make a comparison across the species difficult.

The anabolic steroids could also influence the enzymatic profile in the liver which, in turn, could modulate the metabolic fate of the endogenous hormones, xenobiotics, and environmental carcinogens. Recently, Schulte-Hermann et al. (ref. 39) showed that steroid hormones induced mixed function oxidases and de novo DNA synthesis in the rat liver. Those effects may be relevant to tumor promoting activities of steroid hormones. In addition, 17-alkylated derivatives appear to be hepatotoxic and hepatocarcinogenic in humans (ref. 3). The intrahepatic cholestasis, commonly associated with their administration (ref. 4), could be contributing to the development of these tumors. The promoting effect of bile acids in hepatocarcinogenesis appears possible (refs. 29, 42-43).

The significance of the presence of steroid receptors in the normal and the neoplastic liver and their induction by various agents as contributing factors to hepatocarcinogenesis is not clear (refs. 44-46). Further studies are needed to determine the potential promoting effect of synthetic steroids following exposure to certain environmental hepatocarcinogens such as aflatoxin B_1.

Besides aflatoxins, human hepatitis B virus infection seems to have an important role in the development of liver cancer in humans. Recent studies (refs. 47-48) emphasize that the hepatitis infection represents a major carcinogenic risk to men and women. A possible role for the androgenic anabolic steroids in humans has been suggested (ref. 47). The development of AIDS in an athlete taking anabolic steroids, possibly by sharing injection needles with AIDS-infected persons (ref. 25), suggests also the possibility of a spread of hepatitis B virus infection by the same practice. Since the hepatitis B virus infection occurs in many cases early in life, a number of young users of anabolic steroids may be at risk if sharing the needles. Thus, while experimental and epidemiological evidence is lacking, it would be prudent to screen the intended users of androgenic anabolic steroids for the viral infection.

REFERENCES

1. W. T. London, Hum. Pathol. 12, 1085-1097 (1981).
2. E. T. Mays and W. Christopherson, Seminars in Liver Disease 4, 147-157 (1984).
3. H. A. Haupt and G. D. Rovere, Am. J. Sports Med. 12, 469-484 (1984).
4. K. G. Ishak, Seminars in Liver Disease 1, 116-127 (1981).
5. Committee on Safety of Medicines, Carcinogenicity Tests of Oral Contraceptives, Her Majesty's Stationery Office, London (1972).
6. S. Holck, Wld. Hlth. Statist. Quart. 40, 225-232 (1987).
7. J. Neuberger, D. Forman, R. Doll and R. Williams, Brit. Med. J. 292, 1355-1357 (1986).
8. D. Forman, R. J. Vincent and R. Doll, Brit. Med. J. 292, 1357-1361 (1986).
9. V. Cowart, J. Am. Med. Assoc. 257, 421-427 (1987).
10. J. D. Wilson, Endocrine Rev. 9, 181-199 (1988).
11. R. Hampl, L. Starka, J. Heresova, I. Sipova, Z. Pobisova and J. Marek, J. Steroid Biochem. 24, 349-352 (1986).
12. W. Futterweit and L. Deligdisch, J. Clin. Encocrinol. Metabol. 62, 16-21 (1986).
13. J. T. Roberts and D. M. Essenhigh, Lancet 2, 742 (1986).
14. A. J. Edis and M. Levitt, Med. J. Australia 142, 426-427 (1985).
15. J. Prat, G. J. Gray, P. D. Stolley and J. W. Coleman, J. Am. Med. Assoc. 237, 2322 (1977).
16. J. D. Yager, Jr. and D. S. Fifield, Jr., Carcinogenesis 3, 625-628 (1982).
17. K.V.N. Rao and S. D. Vesselinovitch, Cancer Res. 33, 1625-1627 (1973).
18. N. R. Drinkwater and J. J. Ginsler, Carcinogenesis 157, 1701-1707 (1986).
19. W. F. Friedwald and P. Rous, J. Exptl. Med. 80, 101-126 (1944).
20. I. Berenblum and P. Shubik, Brit. J. Cancer 1, 383-391 (1947).
21. I. Berenblum and P. Shubik, Brit. J. Cancer 3, 109-118 (1949).
22. M. Metzler and G. H. Degen, Arch. Toxicol. Suppl. 10, 251-263 (1987).
23. H. Turani, J. Levi, D. Zevin and E. Kessler, Israel J. Med. Sci. 19, 332-337 (1983).
24. T. Wakabayashi, H. Onda, T. Tada, M. Iijima and Y. Itoh, Acta Pathol. Jpn. 34(5), 1079-1086 (1984).
25. H. M. Sklarek, R. P. Mantovani, E. Erens, D. Heisler, M. S. Niederman and A. M. Fein, New Engl. J. Med. 311, 1701 (1984).
26. S. D. Vesselinovitch, N. Mihailovich and S. Negri, Experimental Hepatocarcinogenesis, pp. 51-62, Plenum Publishing Corp., New York (1988).
27. H. S. Taper, Cancer 42, 462-467 (1978).
28. J. D. Yager and R. Yager, Cancer Res. 40, 3680-3685 (1980).
29. R. C. Cameron, K. Imaida, H. Tsuda and N. Ito, Cancer Res. 42, 2426-2428 (1982).
30. I. R. Wanless and A. Medline, Lab. Invest. 46, 313-320 (1982).
31. S. D. Vesselinovitch and N. Mihailovich, Proc. Am. Assoc. Cancer Res. 23, 91 (1982).
32. J. D. Yager, H. A. Campbell, D. S. Longnecker, B. D. Roebuck and M. C. Benoit, Cancer Res. 44, 3862-3869 (1984).
33. W. Taylor, S. Snowball and M. Lesna, J. Path. 143, 211-218 (1984).
34. M. Lesna and W. Taylor, J. Steroid Biochem. 24, 449-453 (1986).
35. R. L. Noble, Cancer Res. 37, 1929-1933 (1977).
36. R. L. Noble, Canad. Med. Assoc. J. 130, 549 (1984).
37. P. M. Pour and K. Stepan, Cancer Res. 47, 5699-5706 (1987).
38. M. Pollard and P. H. Luckert, J. Natl. Cancer Inst. 77, 583-587 (1986).
39. R. Schulte-Hermann, H. Ochs, W. Bursch and W. Parzefall, Cancer Res. 48, 2462-2468 (1988).
40. M. D. Reuber, Eur. J. Cancer 12, 137-141 (1976).
41. M. Alen, P. Rahkila, M. Reinila and R. Vihko, Am. J. Sports Med. 15, 357-361 (1987).
42. H. Tsuda, T. Masui, K. Imaida, S. Fusushima and N. Ito, Gann 75, 871-875 (1984).
43. H. Tsuda, M. Asamoto, M. Kagawa, S. Swagawa, K. Inoue, M. Inui and N. Ito, Carcinogenesis 9, 1103-1105 (1988).
44. M. J. Iqbal, A. A. Colletta and S. H. Valyani, Anticancer Res. 7, 773-780 (1987).
45. M. L. Wilkinson, Anticancer Res. 7, 1071-1078 (1987).
46. J. L. Ostrowski, P. M. Ingleton, J.C.E. Underwood and M. A. Parsons, Gastroenterology 94, 1193-1200 (1988).
47. Di Bisceglie (moderator), V. K. Rustgi, J. H. Hoffnagle, G. M. Dusheiko and M. T. Lotze (discussants), Ann. Int. Med. 108, 390-401 (1988).
48. J. N. Gru, Carcinogenesis 9, 697-703 (1988).

Potentiating effect of carnitine on the *in vitro* methacholine-induced relaxation of masseteric arteries

V.Bettini, F.Ceccherelli*, G.Fantin, G.Lo Castro, R.Martino, G.Pulliero**, V.Tegazzin*, P.Ton

Human Physiology Dept., University of Padua (Italy)
* Anaesthesiology and Intensive Care Unit Dept., Univ.of Padua (Italy)
** Geriatrics Dept., Ospedale Civile USL 23, Monselice, Padua (Italy)

Abstract - It is known that carnitine has cholinomimetic effects. We investigated "in vitro" the influence of this substance on the masseteric arteries segments relaxation, induced by methacholine, (Mch), specific muscarinic agent. This effect was constantly suppressed by atropine or prifinium bromide. Carnitine invariably increased the above-mentioned relaxation; this facilitating effect was decreased or suppressed by atropine or prifinium bromide, but usually it was not weakened by indomethacin or lysine acetylsalicylate. While prostaglandin mediation appears improbable in the genesis of the observed potentiation, it is possible to suppose that carnitine increases the response of the preparations to Mch by sensitizing the muscarinic receptors, which can stimulate the release of the ERDF (Endothelial Relaxing Factor) from the wall of the vessels used, as it has been reported for other tributary arteries of the skeletal muscles. Therefore, masseteric arteries could represent a suitable model to study the functional properties of these muscles. Furthermore, it is possible to support that carnitine administration has two advantages:
- a short-term advantage, because it increases the blood flow of the working muscle;
- a long-term advantage, because it protects the vascular endothelium and it prevents from any thrombotic phenomena, therefore it counteracts the onset of atherosclerotic injuries.

Key words: Masseteric artery, Carnitine, Methacholine.

INTRODUCTION

The fact that both carnitine and its acetylated derivative are able to excite the cortical neurons in cats, which is an occurrence very similar to that observed by using acetylcholine (Ach), together with the circumstance that all these effects are suppressed by atropine (1), may suggest that carnitine has cholinomimetic properties. These properties have been confirmed recently by our previous studies on the vascular (2) and visceral (3) smooth muscle of the mammals, proving that carnitine potentiates the contractile responses of Ach and methacholine (Mch) (4), and that this potentiating effect is reduced or suppressed in the presence of Ca^{++} -antagonists (2,3).
We attribute these facilitating influences to the ability of carnitine to sensitize the muscarinic receptors promoting the contractility of smooth muscle fibers - as it is well known(5, 7) - by favouring both the Ca^{++} entrance through the cell membrane and the ion release from the intracellular sites of storage (8).

Furthermore, we observed that carnitine "in vitro" enhances the Ach effects also in some tributary vessels of the skeletal muscles (9), where the neurotransmitter induces relaxation instead of contraction (10).

The cholinomimetic properties of carnitine in those vessels would receive further experimental support if this substance favoured also the relaxation induced by a specific muscarinic agent, such as methacholine (Mch).

With this study we intend to verify this possibility by investigating the influence of carnitine on the Mch-induced relaxation of calf masseteric arteries isolated preparations in the presence of anti-muscarinic drugs or inhibitors of the prostaglandin synthesis.

It seems to be clear that it is important not only an investigation on the altered resistance to the blood flow in muscular area, but also an analysis on the influence of this resistance on the cholinergic fibers activities controlling the tonus of vascular wall in the skeletal muscles (10), and an investigation on the sensitivity of these vessels to the above-mentioned nervous fibers neurotransmitter, because the blood perfusion during the muscular work is of paramount importance.

MATERIALS AND METHODS

This study was performed on 100 isolated preparations from calf masseteric arteries,according to our well specialized and standardized technique (11).

The masseteric artery segments were withdrawn from a tract of about 5 cm corresponding to the position of the masseter muscle; the masseteric artery underwent perpendicular cuts to its longitudinal axis to form several rings, subsequently opened. The obtained segments, long about 1 cm each, were sewn in series by a silk thread, sealing symmetric points of two contiguous edges. The seam has been performed in two different points of the contiguous edges, so that it was possible to take the maximum advantage from the traction a segment exerted on the other. The obtained band was fastened on one side into a thermostatic bath, and on the other side to a mechanical electric transductor. After this procedure, every preparation was placed in a thermostatic bath containing 100 ml of physiological solution at 38°C, where a gaseous mixture of O_2 (95 p.c.) and CO_2 (5 p.c.) was made to gurgle. The composition of the physiological solution (Locke type) was as follows: 154 mM/l NaCl, 6 mM/l NaHCO$_3$, 5.5 mM/l KCl, 2.2 mM/l CaCl$_2$, 10 mM/l glucose. The pH value was 6.9-7.0 while gurgling; the constancy of this value has been examined throughout the study. The mechanical activity was recorded by means of a strain-gauge semi-isometric transducer (DY1 U. Basile, Milano) connected with a paper-fed printing recorder (2 channel Recorder Gemini, U. Basile, Milano). After this treatment, the preparations rested in a standard physiological solution for 3-4 hours until they reached a spontaneous steady length; once obtained, we tested their reactivity to Mch. The preparations not complying with the concentration of 1 µg/ml of this substance were discarded. Washes with Ringer-Locke standard solutions were performed after each assay. For any detail, refer to our previous study (11).

The substances here used were: Methacholine (Sigma); Atropine sulphate (Merck); Prifinium Bromide (IBI); Indomethacin (Chiesi); Lysine acetylsalicylate (Maggioni); L-Carnitine (Sigma-Tau).

RESULTS

1 In the masseteric artery preparations placed in Ringer-Locke standard solution, Mch (0.01-0.05 ug/ml) invariably induced relaxation (Fig. 1a). This effect was never modified by the treatment with indomethacin or lysine acetylsalicylate (1-4 ug/ml); as for higher concentrations of indomethacin or lysine acetylsalicylate (10-40 ug/ml) in some case we observed an increased tonus and decreased responses to Mch of the preparations. These phenomena, however, were of small entity (Fig. 1).

2 Atropin and prifinium bromide (with 0.05 and 0.08 µg/ml concentration) did not modify appreciably the Mch-induced relaxation, whereas at higher concentration (0.5-1 µg/ml) the relaxation was reduced or even abolished (Fig. 2). Atropine or prifinium bromide (0.5-1 µg/ml), tested separately, steadily caused slight decrease of tonus of the preparations.

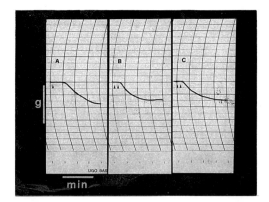

Fig.1. Response of masseteric artery preparation, placed in Ringer-Locke standard solution:
a) 0.05 µg/ml Mch, control. b) 0.05 µg/ml Mch, in the presence of indomethacin (40 µg/ml).
c) 0.05 µg/ml Mch, in the presence of lysine acetylsalicylate (40 µg/ml).

In a), the Mch addition corresponds to the arrows. In b), the indomethacin addition corresponds to the first arrow, and the Mch addition to the second arrow. In c), the lysine acetylsalicylate addition corresponds to the first arrow, and the Mch addition to the second arrow. Washed in Ringer-Locke standard solution after each assay.

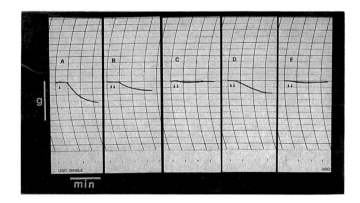

Fig.2. Response of masseteric artery preparation placed in Ringer-Locke standard solution:
a) 0.05 µg/ml Mch, control. b) 0.05 µg/ml Mch, in the presence of atropine (0.5 µg/ml). c) 0.05 µg/ml Mch, in the presence of atropine (1 µg/ml). d) 0.05 µg/ml Mch, in the presence of prifinium bromide (0.6 µg/ml). e) 0.05 ug/ml Mch, in the presence of prifinium bromide (1 µg/ml).

In a), the Mch addition corresponds to the arrows. In b) and c), the atropine addition corresponds to the first arrow, and the Mch addition to the second arrow. In d) and e), the prifinium bromide addition corresponds to the first arrows, and the Mch addition to the second arrows. Washed in Ringer-Locke standard solution after each assay.

3   Carnitine (0.5-1 µg/ml) never induced appreciable variation of the tonus of the preparation. Nevertheless, in all cases, it increased the Mch-induced relaxation (0.01-0.05 µg/ml) the magnitude of this effect is proportional to the carnitine concentration used (Fig.3, 4). In fact, the treatment with indomethacin or lysine acetyl-salicylate (1-40 µg/ml) never modified the magnitude of the carnitine-induced potentiation of Mch (Fig. 5).

4   Atropine and prifinium bromide (used at concentration not modifying the Mch-induced relaxation of the controls) generally attenuated or, in some case, suppressed the carnitine--induced potentiation of the response to Mch (Fig.6).

110 V. BETTINI *ET AL.*

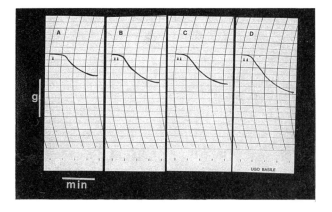

Fig.3. Response of masseteric artery preparation in Ringer-Locke standard solution: a)0.05 µg/ml Mch, control. b,c,d)0.05 µg/ml Mch in the presence of carnitine (respectively 0.5--0.75-1 ug/ml).

In a), the Mch addition corresponds to the arrow. In b, c, d) the carnitine addition corresponds to the first arrow, and the Mch addition to the second arrow. Washed in Ringer-Locke standard solution after each assay.

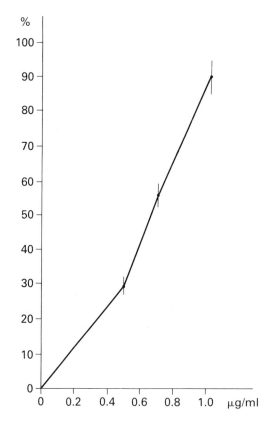

Fig.4. Mean percent increase (±SD) of our preparations relaxation inducing responses to Mch (0.05 µg/ml), according to carnitine concentration ranging between 0.5 and 1 µg/ml. The points relative to each carnitine concentration represent the average of 20 experiments.

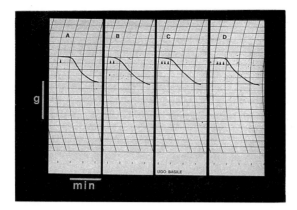

Fig.5. Response of masseteric artery preparation in Ringer-Locke standard solution:
a) 0.05 µg/ml Mch, control. b) 0.05 µg/ml Mch, in the presence of carnitine (0.5 µg/ml).
c) 0.05 µg/ml Mch, in the presence of indomethacin (40 µg/ml) and carnitine (0.5 µg/ml).
d) 0.05 µg/ml Mch, in the presence of lysine acetylsalicylate (40 µg/ml) and carnitine (0.5 µg/ml).

In a), the Mch addition corresponds to the arrow. In b), the carnitine addition corresponds to the first arrow, and the Mch addition to the second arrow. In c), the indomethacin addition to the second arrow, and the Mch addition to the third arrow. In d), the lysine acetylsalicylate addition corresponds to the first arrow, the carnitine addition to the second arrow, and the Mch addition to the third arrow. Washed in Ringer-Locke standard solution after each assay.

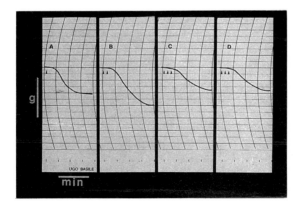

Fig.6. Response of masseteric artery preparation placed in Ringer-Locke standard solution:
a) 0.05 µg/ml Mch, control. b) 0.05 µg/ml Mch, in the presence of carnitine (0.70 µg/ml).
c) 0.05 µg/ml Mch, in the presence of atropine (0.08 ug/ml) and carnitine (0.7 µg/ml).

In a), the Mch addition corresponds to the arrow. In b), the carnitine addition corresponds to the first arrow, and the Mch addition to the second arrow. In c), the atropine addition corresponds to the first arrow, the carnitine addition to the second arrow, the Mch addition to the third arrow. Washed in Ringer-Locke standard solution after each assay.

DISCUSSION

The observation reported here that the Mch-induced relaxation of the smooth muscle of the masseteric artery is abolished by atropine or prifinium bromide, well-known muscarinic antago- nists, indicated that the muscarinic receptors mediate not only the contraction of some vessels (2) or visceral smooth muscles (3), but also the observed relaxation. These results confirm the literature data about other vascular segments (12).

Moreover the fact that atropine or prifinium bromide reduce or abolish the carnitine - increas- ing effect at concentration not modifying significantly the relaxation in the controls,   in our opinion represents another experimental confirmation of the hypothesis of carnitine choli- nomimetic activity (1, 2), already confirmed by other Authors. The pharmacological interruption of the prostaglandin synthesis, in this case induced by indomethacin or lysine acetylsalicyla- te, only sometimes and quite unapprecciably modifying the potentiating effect of carnitine, leads us to deem the vasodilator prostaglandin mediation the most probable factor causing this effect. The exclusion of a prostaglandin mediation could be accepted also because of   the results of our previous studies (9), where we observed that the potentiating vasodilator effect of Ach induced by carnitine did not undergo important variations in the presence of the above- -mentioned cyclo-oxygenase-inhibitors.

As it was stated in previous studies (9, 13) on the Ach-induced relaxation of various vascular segments, this observation does not give us any suggestion about the possible mechanism   by which Mch and Ach cause the relaxation of the vascular smooth muscle.

The causes of this phenomenon could be due to the ability of both substances to promote the in- tracellular sequestration of calcium and/or the extrusion of the same ion through the membrane of the myocells, or by increasing the cell permeability to the potassium, or by activating the release of EDRF (Endothelial Relaxing Factor). None of these hypotheses can be discarded reasonably. The information in literature (14,15) on the first mechanism is quite contradictory about the possibility that the stimulation of muscarinic receptors increases the intracellular cAMP content which, as it is known, causes the vascular muscle relaxation by the above - men- tioned removal of calcium ions (16). This problem is at present the object of a careful investigation. Both the second and the third mechanisms, on the contrary, are   supported by literature.

CONCLUSIONS AND PERSPECTIVES

Our experimental finding, according to which masseteric arteries become relaxed after adminis- tration of two muscarinic agents, as different tributary arteries of the skeletal muscle (12) were said to do, shows that the kind of vessel, here considered, represents a suitable model for the study of muscular circulatory districts. Therefore, these observations offer interest- ing indications for the long-term usefulness of carnitine, and can be a different approach from the conventional biochemical approach to the study of the biological activity of carni- tine. First of all, concerning the possible short-term advantages of the carnitine adminis- tration, they are important for those who practise sports or must face heavy muscular works. As a matter of fact, from the assumption that this practice is accompanied, or even preceded, by a skeletal muscle vasodilation (10) mediated by cholinergic sympathic fibers (10),derives the fact that the sensitization of muscarinic receptors caused by carnitine can enhance the vasodilator effect of Ach released by these fibers, thus it can facilitate the blood flow of the working muscle. It is clear that this effect cannot only improve the muscular performance but also delay any tiring phenomena. In the second place, carnitine administration   can have also a long-term usefulness not only concerning the muscular function. As a matter of fact, it results that the stimulation of muscarinic receptors helps the EDRF to be released, which reduces not only the tonus of the vessel wall, but also the platelet aggregation (18), thus it represents an aid in thrombotic phenomena and in vascular endothelium injuries,   as it was stated by Virchow (19), in the past century, and other Authors (20-25) up to now.

Therefore it does not seem to be groundless the statement that carnitine can represent reaso- nably, by activating muscarinic receptors, a defence factor of the vascular endothelium and that it can be considered as a vaso-protective, anti-hypertensive and antithrombotic agent (18).

We are grateful to AIRAS for the collaboration.

REFERENCES

1. F. Falchetto, G. Kato, L. Provin, Can. J. Physiol. Pharmacol., 49, 1 (1971).
2. V. Bettini, C. Catozzo, R. Martino, F. Mayellaro, L. Munari, V. Tegazzin, P. Ton, Acta Vitaminol. Enzymol., 7, 61 (1985).
3. V. Bettini, R. Martino, M. Norani, E. Legrenzi, P. Ton, Il farmaco, 41, 530 (1986).
4. V. Bettini, P. Fabro, L. Munari, P.F.Munari, P. Ton, M. Tura, Biol.Cont., 1987 (in press).
5. H. Kuriyama, Smooth Muscles, 171, Edward Arnold London (1981).
6. V. Bettini, G. Gamba, E. Legrenzi, F. Mayellaro, L. Munari, Biol.Med., 5, 163 (1983).
7. V. Bettini, G. Gamba, E. Legrenzi, G.F. Marinelli, F. Mayellaro, Biol. Med., 5, 147 (1983).
8. V. Bettini, M.G. Marigonda, R. Martino, G. Pulliero, P. Ton, 2nd Cardiovascular Pharmaco therapy Int. symposium, San Francisco (1987).
9. V. Bettini, E. De Varda, B. Guerra, G. Pulliero, P. Ton, Cardiologia, 32, 1039 (1987).
10. P. Lindgren, Acta Physiol. Scand., 35, 9 (1955).
11. M. Midrio, V. Bettini, Arch. Sci. Biol., 52, 182 (1968).
12. H. Kitagawa, P. Takeda, H. Kahei, Eur. J. Pharmacol., 133, 57 (1987).
13. V. Bettini, G. Cibotto, L. Munari, P. Ton, Riunione del gruppo di studio "Cardiologia Sperimentale", Gardone Riviera, Brescia, Aprile 1986.
14. S.M. Sand, T.A. Meyert, M.V. Rikenberg, Biochem. Biophys. acta, 302, 267 (1973).
15. R.B. Nilsson, G. Andersson, G. Ralf, S. Borjesson, L. Machedova, E. Mohme-Lundhalun, L. Lundhalun, Excitation-contraction coupling in smooth muscle, 189, North Holland (1977).
16. J.G. Hardman, Smooth muscle, 249, Edward Arnold London (1981).
17. T.B. Bolton, Smooth muscle, 210, Edward Arnold London (1981).
18. J.R. Vane, R.J. Gryglewski, R.M. Batting, TIPS, 8, 491 (1987).
19. R. Virchow, Gesammelte Abbandungen zur Wissenschaftlichen Medizin, Frankfurt am Mein, 458 (1856).
20. J.E. French, Int. Rew. Exp. Pathol., 5, 253 (1966).
21. R. Ross, J. Glosmet, N. Engl. J. Med., 295, 369 (1976).
22. R. Ross, Atherosclerosis, 1, 293 (1981).
23. R. Ross, Harvey Lec., 77, 161 (1983).
24. R. Ross, A. Faggiotto, D. Bowen-Pope, E. Raines, Circulation, 70, 77 (1984).
25. S.M. Kruth, Science, 227, 1243 (1985).

Changes of liver, testicles and muscles of experimental animals at training, affected by anabolic steroids

Prof. dr Stanoje Stanojevic, dr Slobodan Musulin

FK "Crvena Zvezda", Beograd

Physicians for sport, trainers and sportists have expected from medicine to find something for speeding up the albumen synthesis to restitute quantity changes at improvement of sportists working capacity. The basic good results in this field was achieved at separation of compounds with steroid characteristics, so-called anabolic hormones, which in organism stimulated the albumen synthesis.

Many hormones make anabolic influence in organism, but in view of the strength of effectiveness male sexual hormone-androgens are separated as well as their synthetic products. Application of androgen hormones in the form of testosterone preparations and other is not accepted because of their explicit androgen influence. The situation has considerably changed when synthetic preparations of steroids with weaker androgenic influence has appeared in the market, but with preserved and maybe even with strengthen anabolic characteristics as Dianabol, Durabolin, Deca-Durabolin and other. Knowing this, sportists widely use anabolic steroids with aim of getting better results having increased muscle mass. Anabolic steroids are especially used in sports in which strength is dominant. According to experimental works of Johnson and O'Shea, they proved that the anabolic influence of androgenic hormones in humans may be seen in increased azote retention in albumen tissues. This retention of azote has an affect on growing and on speed of albumen synthesis, and decreasing of amino acid catabolism, which causes increase of body weight. They also proved that if the quantity of albumen in nutrient is limited, anabolic steroids do not influence the growth of azote bilans, or the maintaining of azote in albumen tissue. How physical strain causes increase of energy exchange and albumen, this will be equal effort effect of utilization of anabolic steroids by sportists who are using them, depend on changing of activity of albumen metabolism and of its quantity in food. Thanks to this process, androgens entered into sport as substance "without which there are no results."

To prove this, experiments were made on male Albino Rats, and lasted 6 months. The animals were divided into 4 groups (10 rats in each group) as follows:
    A. Control
    B1. Animals which trained
    B2. Animals which received Deca-Durabolin injection
    B3. Animals which trained and received Deca-Durabolin injection

The animals trained 3 times a week 5 minutes each time, totalling 77 days, and at the same time received Deca-Durabolin injection 1.5 mg each day, which makes 115,5 mg the experimental period.

Before and after the experiment the body weight of animals was measured. After the experiment the animals were immolated and the liver, left testicle and left m. quadriceps femoris of hind paw were taken out for analysis.

The body weights of all animals were the same before testing (185 gr) in all groups. After training the growths of weight were the most in animals which trained (B1), 294 gr. in average, or 163%, somewhat less in group A with 292 gr or 162%, then group B2 with 223 gr or 120% and the smallest growth of weight was in group B3 with 189 gr or 105%.

On the basis of analysis of liver slide it is obvious that the biggest growth
of weight had the group B1, with circulation of individual values of 6,50-
7,58 gr, in group B3 6,40-7,12 gr., group B2 5,00-5,70 gr., and the individual values in group A were from 5,00-5,20 gr. The most obvious histologic
changes were observed on liver slide of group B3, in the form of hyperemia,
multiplied gall channel in porter places, as well as parenhymatosic degenera-
tion of hepatocytes. The same result, but less expressively is observed on
slide of group B2, while on slide of group A and B1 normal configurations.

The most obvious changes are observed by the affect of anabolic steroids on
testicles. The biggest average weight of testicles had the animals in group
A with individual values of 2,45-2,80 gr., while normal values had the
animals in group B3, with individual values of 1,50-2,10 gr. The slide of
group B1 had individual value of 1,84-2,22 gr. and the slide of group B2 of
1,80-2,10 gr. However the histologic results on slide of group B3 contained
in slightly thickened capsule, hyperemia, slight atrophy of germinative
epithel/spermatogonic I, II, III class/and multiplied sertoli sincicijum.
The slide of testicles of group B2 had the same changes but less expressively.
Changes on slides of group A and B1 are not observed i.e. configurations are
normal.

Since the animals of group B1 and B3 trained and received Deca-Durabolin (B3)
changes are observed on their muscles. Namely, biggest average weight had
the animals which trained (B1) with individual values from 1,12-1,60, while
the lowest individual values had the animals in group B3 from 0,80-1,45 gr.
slides of group A had individual values from 1,15-1,30 gr. and group B2 from
1,10-1,58 gr. On histologic slide of group B3 hypertrophy of muscle tissues
was observed, but with preserved sarcolemma and without changes on cell

(a) Muscles B_1

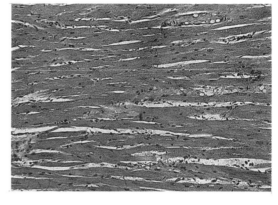

(b) muscles B_2

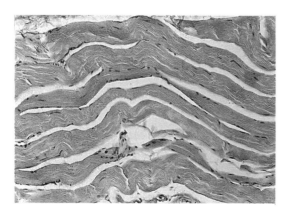

(c) muscles B_3

nucleus, while on slide of group B1 hypertrophy of myofibrils are observed after training.

With this experimental work we have tried to point out the harmful effect of anabolic steroids on organism, with an advice to sportists not to use them, but to take more seriously trainings, sport food, and physiologic means for recovery.

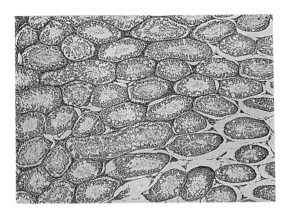

(d) testicle B$_1$

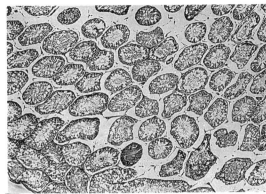

(e) testicle B$_2$

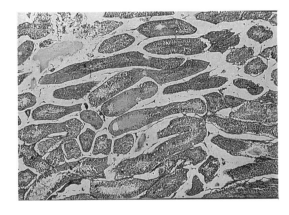

(f) testicle B$_3$

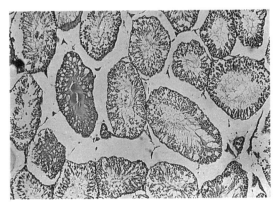
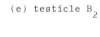

(g) testicle B$_3$

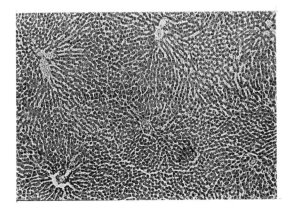

(h) liver B$_2$

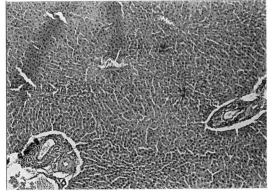

(i) liver B$_3$

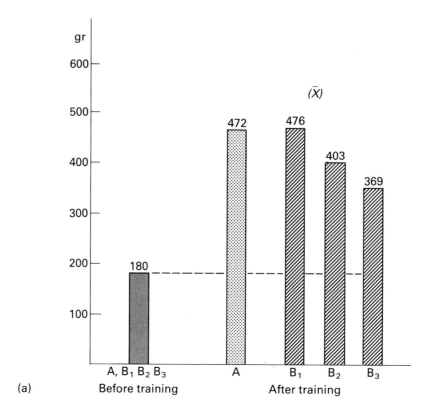

(a)

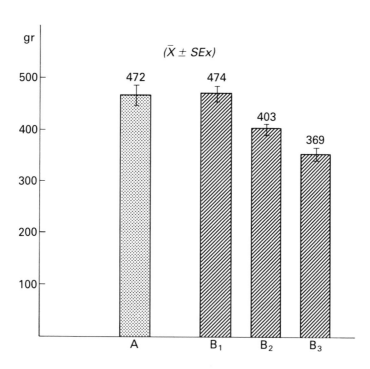

(b)

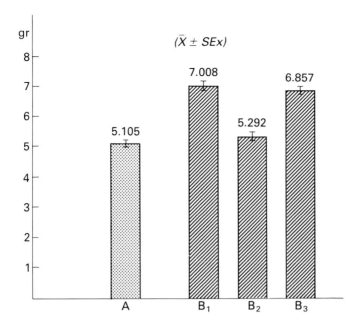

(c)

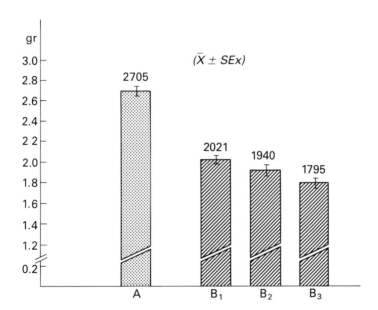

(d)

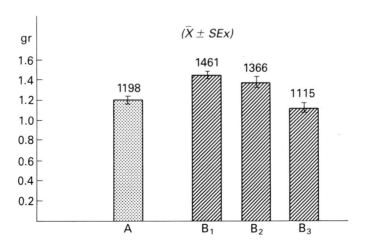

(e)

Effects of anabolizing androgens on hepatic monooxygenase activities

A. Saborido, J. Vila, J.M. Odriozola and A. Megías

Department of Biochemistry, Faculties of Chemistry and Biology
Universidad Complutense, 28040 Madrid, Spain

Abstract - The influence on liver function of the administration of high doses of the anabolizing androgens fluoxymesterone and mestanolone has been investigated in sedentary and trained male rats. After treatment, the mean values of serum alanine aminotransferase (GPT), aspartate aminotransferase (GOT) and alkaline phosphatase remained within normal range in all groups. These results suggest that liver function was not impaired. However, the studies performed on liver microsomal fraction demonstrated that the anabolizing androgens, with or without exercise, were able to reduce significantly the levels of cytochrome P-450 and cytochrome b_5, as well as the activities of their associated reductases. Furthermore, the detoxifying activities aniline hydroxylase and 7-ethoxycoumarin deethylase, cytochrome P-450-dependent, were differently affected: the former was significantly reduced by both steroids and the latter underwent a slight decrease when compared with controls. It can be concluded that prolonged high-dose anabolic steroids ingestion could induce alterations of the liver function that are not adequately reflected on the serum parameters commonly evaluated.

INTRODUCTION

Anabolizing androgens are synthetic derivatives of testosterone widely used by athletes in an attempt of improving physical performance. Although contradictory results have been reported about the beneficial effects of these compounds in sports, irrespective of their utility, the possible side effects involving health risks have also to be considered. Thus, the high doses taken orally by the athletes could be regarded as a heavy load on liver metabolism, since this organ is the major site where steroid hormones and xenobiotics are biotransformed. In the case of oral anabolizing androgens, alquil groups introduced in the 17α-position to retard the degradation by the liver seem to be associated with hepatotoxic effects. Minor or no changes of the level of enzymes and metabolites related to liver function have been detected in the serum of athletes using different anabolic steroids and this fact has been con considered indicative of a slight impairment of hepatic function (ref. 1). However, the possibility of not detected damage to liver cells in conventional liver function test can not be excluded on the basis of these data.Taking into account the importance of the hepatic drug-metabolizing systems in relation to hepatotoxic and carcinogenic processes, we have studied the effects of high doses of oral anabolizing androgens on the levels and enzymatic activities of monooxygenase system in microsomes from liver of sedentary and trained rats.

MATERIALS AND METHODS

Anabolizing androgens. Fluoxymesterone (11β,17β-dihydroxy-9α-fluoro-17α-methyl-4-androsten-3-one) and mestanolone (17β-hydroxy-17α-methyl-5α-androstan-3-one) were obtained from Sigma.

Training program and treatment. 36 male Wistar rats (initial weight 116 g $\pm$ 4) were randomly assigned to one of two groups: sedentary and trained. Trained animals underwent regular (5 days/wk) moderate-intensity exercise (25 m/min,

0% gradient, 45 min/day) on a treadmill for 12 weeks. At the beginning of the fifth training week, when maximal exercise intensity was reached, both groups were randomly subdivided into the following groups: control, fluoxymesterone--treated and mestanolone-treated groups. The animals selected for steroid treatment received 2 mg steroid/ kg body weight orally 5 days a week, forming a suspension in 1 ml of water.

Blood and liver sampling. After 12 weeks of training, animals were fasted overnight and, under ether anesthesia, blood was collected by cardiac puncture. The liver was perfused in situ via the portal vein with ice-cold 0.9% saline solution to remove residual blood, immediately frozen in liquid nitrogen and stored at -70°C until use.

Serum analyses. The activities of serum enzymes: aspartate aminotransferase, alanine aminotransferase and alkaline phosphatase were analysed from serum samples stored at -40°C, using the reagents of Boehringer Mannheim. Total and direct bilirubin were determined in fresh serum by a colorimetric procedure (Ames, Miles Lab.).

Measurements in liver microsomes. Liver microsomes were obtained by differential centrifugation as described by Steward et al. (ref. 2), with slight modifications. Microsomal protein was estimated by the method of Lowry et al. (ref. 3). Microsomal fractions were assayed as follows: aniline hydroxylase according to Imai et al. (ref. 4), 7-ethoxycoumarin deethylase by the fluorometric procedure of Aitio (ref. 5), total cytochrome P-450 and cytochrome b_5 as described by Omura and Sato (ref. 6,7), NADPH-cytochrome P-450 reductase and NADH-cytochrome b_5 reductase according to the methods of Phillips and Langdon (ref. 8) and Mihara and Sato (ref. 9), respectively. One unit of activity is defined as that causing the transformation of 1 μmol of substrate per minute under the conditions described.

Analysis of data. In these experiments, mean values of data were compared with the unpaired Student's t-test (two-tailed).

RESULTS AND DISCUSSION

Effects of exercise
Although we have employed a moderate-intensity exercise program, the 12 weeks of mild-endurance training were effective in inducing the well-characterized increase in the skeletal muscle mitochondrial enzyme succinate dehydrogenase, in addition to a significant decrease (14%) in the body weight of the trained rats when compared with the sedentary animals (data not shown).

Serum parameters
After the treatment with anabolizing androgens, the mean values of serum transaminases and alkaline phosphatase remained within normal range in all groups, whereas a significant increase was detected in total bilirubin in the sedentary and trained animals treated with fluoxymesterone (Fig. 1). These results are consistent with those obtained by Alén (ref. 1) with power athletes who self-administered very high doses of testosterone and anabolic steroids for 26 weeks and with those reported by Ballarin et al. (ref. 10) with well-trained middle-distance runners receiving therapeutic doses of stanozolol. Therefore, values of common serum hepatic parameters, in rats and in athletes, suggest that liver function is midly or not impaired due to the high-dose anabolizing androgens administration.

Microsomal mixed-function oxidase activities
In spite of the above results, it has been reported that anabolic steroids, when administered to adult female rats, increased the activity of several enzymes in liver microsomes (ref. 11). Furthermore, oral testosterone treatment in normal men appeared to induce the hepatic drug-metabolizing sustems, since intravenous antipyrine and testosterone half-lives decreased significantly (ref. 12). Taking into account the involvement of liver mixed-function oxidases (MFO) in adaptation to environmental changes, in relationship xenobiotics-disease and in the metabolism of essential regulatory molecules, it is clear the importance of determining whether alterations occur in these enzymatic systems as a result of anabolizing androgens ingestion.

The treatment with fluoxymesterone and mestanolone affected the two microsomal drug-metabolizing activities studied differently (Fig. 2). While aniline

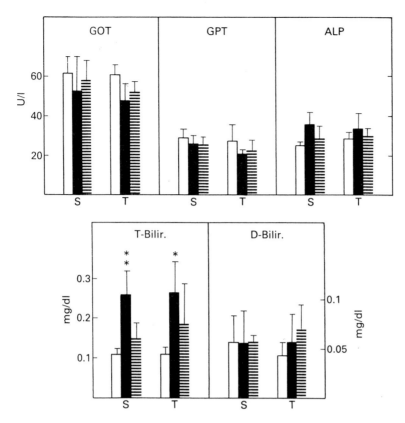

Fig. 1. Aspartate aminotransferase (GOT), alanine aminotrans-
    ferase (GPT) and alkaline phosphatase (ALP) activities, and
    total bilirubin (T-Bilir.) and direct bilirubin (D-Bilir.)
    levels in serum of sedentary (S) and trained (T) rats.
    Values are means $\pm$ SD (n=5-6); $*$ P < 0.01, $**$ P < 0.001 com-
    pared to the respective control group.
        ☐ control groups.
        ■ fluoxymesterone-treated groups.
        ≡ mestanolone-treated groups.

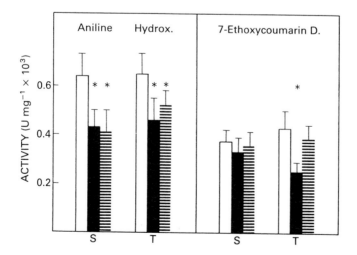

Fig. 2. Aniline hydroxylase and 7-ethoxycoumarin deethylase
    activities in liver microsomes of sedentary and trained rats.
    Results are expressed as in Fig. 1.

hydroxylase was significantly reduced by both steroids, 7-ethoxycoumarin deethylase was only slightly decreased when compared with controls. Exercise did
not introduce further changes.The different degree of reduction in these activities is not unexpected considering that distinct isozymes of cytochrome
P-450 are involved in the two reactions (ref. 13).

Cytochrome P-450 and associated proteins

In order to ascertain whether alterations in the mixed-function oxidase activities were the reflection of changes in hepatic microsomal cytochrome P-450
level and/or in other proteins involved in the transfer of electrons to this
cytochrome, we have determined the levels and activities of the components of
the microsomal electron transport pathways. Results are shown in Fig. 3.
Fluoxymesterone as well as mestanolone caused a significant decrease in the
level of cytochrome P-450, the main catalytic component of the hepatic MFO
system. Similar reductions were observed in cytochrome b_5 level and in the
activities of the reductases associated with both hemoproteins. This genera-
lized diminution of the hepatic microsomal components of drug-metabolizing
systems was slightly smoothed in the trained animals.

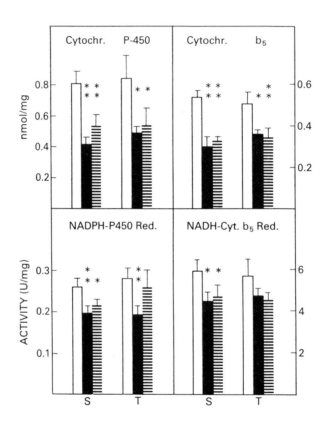

Fig. 3. Cytochrome P-450 and cytochrome b_5 contents and
NADPH-cytochrome P-450 reductase and NADH-cytochrome b_5
reductase activities in liver microsomes of sedentary and
trained rats. Results are expressed as in Fig. 1.

In conclusion, the present data show that the prolonged ingestion of high
doses of anabolizing androgens can originate alterations in the hepatic capacity to metabolize drugs, without reflection on conventional serum parameters.
It is well documented the fact that in rat liver, endogenous androgens and
synthetic glucocorticoids are able to induce certain drug-metabolizing enzymes and to depress others (ref. 13,14). The modifications of these systems
may alter the sensibility of the liver to chemical injure. In this context,
marked decreases in cytochrome P-450 mixed-function oxidase systems are reported to occur in primary hepatomas in rats as well as in humans (ref. 15,16)
indicating that a real health risk exists in the employ of anabolizing androgens.

Acknowledgments: Supported by grants from Consejo Superior de Deportes and Universidad Complutense.

REFERENCES

1. A. Alén, Brit. J. Sports Med. 19, 15-20 (1985).
2. A.R. Steward, G.A. Dannan, P.S. Guzelian and F.P. Guengerich, Mol. Pharmacol. 27, 125-132 (1985).
3. O.H. Lowry, N.J. Rosenbrough, A.L. Farr and R.J. Randall, J. Biol. Chem. 193, 265-275 (1951).
4. Y. Imai, A. Ito and R. Sato, J. Biochem. 60, 417-428 (1966).
5. A. Aitio, Anal. Biochem. 85, 488-491 (1978).
6. T. Omura and R. Sato, J. Biol. Chem. 239, 2370-2378 (1964).
7. T. Omura and R. Sato, J. Biol. Chem. 239, 2379-2385 (1964).
8. A.H. Phillips and R.G. Langdon, J. Biol. Chem. 237, 2652-2660 (1962).
9. K. Mihara and R. Sato, Methods Enzymol. 52, 102-108 (1978).
10. E. Ballarin, C. Guglielmini, S. Martinelli, I. Casoni, C. Borsetto, P.G. Ziglio and F. Conconi, Int. J. Sports Med. 7, 302-306 (1986).
11. J. Booth and J.R. Gillette, J. Pharmacol. Exp. Ther. 137, 374-379 (1962).
12. S.G. Johnsen, J.P. Kampmann, E. P. Bennett and F.S. Jørgensen, Clin. Pharmacol. Ther. 20, 233-237 (1976).
13. J.P. Whitlock Jr., Ann. Rev. Pharmacol. Toxicol. 26, 333-369 (1986).
14. D.L. Simmons, P. McQuiddy and C.B. Kasper, J. Biol. Chem. 262, 326-332 (1987).
15. M. ElMouelhi, M.S. Didolkar, E.G. Elias, F.P. Guengerich and F.C. Kaufmann, Cancer Res. 47, 460-466 (1987)
16. D.L. Stout and F.F. Becker, Cancer Res. 47, 963-966 (1987).

Effect of fluoxymesterone administration on adrenal steroidogenesis in dependence of the sex

A. Megías, S. Abarca, A. Saborido and R. García

Department of Biochemistry. Faculty of Chemistry and Biology.
Universidad Complutense. 28040 Madrid. Spain.

Abstract- Sedentary male and female rats have been subjected to
an oral treatment with the anabolizing androgen fluoxymesterone
for a five-weeks period and the effects on adrenal steroidogenesis have been evaluated. Control and treated male rats exibit-
ed similar serum corticoids levels, whereas about a 45% reduction was observed in treated female rats when compared with the
respective control values. In male rats, serum levels of HDL-
cholesterol and esterified cholesterol present in the adrenal
gland did not change after fluoxymesterone administration but
a significant decrease of both parameters was found in treated female rats.   These results suggest that fluoxymesterone reduces adrenal steroidogenesis by lowering the availability of
substrate although other additional mechanisms can not be excluded.

INTRODUCTION

Androgenic anabolic steroids seem to cause improvements in muscular strength
or athletic performance and to prevent overtraining syndrome in endurance events.
This is a condition caused by prolonged intense training which, at least partly, may be due to a disturbed balance between anabolic and catabolic hormones
(ref. 1). In fact, intense physical exercise promotes an increase in plasma
cortisol and a decrease in plasma testosterone (ref. 2), leading to an enhancement of the catabolic effects of glucocorticoids. High doses of anabolic steroids could protect skeletal muscle from these harmful effects. On the other
hand, it has been shown that long-term testosterone administration to male rats
provokes a time-dependent atrophy of the adrenal cortex, increases in the levels
of circulating ACTH, decreases in the activity of key enzymes of adrenal steroids biosynthesis and a reduction in plasma corticosterone concentration (ref.
3). However, the administration of testosterone and androgenic anabolic steroids to power athletes during 6 weeks of training did not change serum cortisol
levels, although a reduced serum ACTH concentration was observed possibly due
to a corticoid-like effect of some of the anabolic steroids taken in high
doses (ref. 4). The reasons for these discrepancies are unclear, but it is con-
ceivable the masking of the possible effects of anabolic steroids on adrenal
steroidogenesis by the simultaneous intense training program. Also, the differences in the androgenic and anabolic properties between synthetic androgens
and testosterone could explain these apparently contradictory results.

Therefore, it seemed worthwhile to study the effect of an anabolic steroid
(fluoxymesterone) on adrenal endocrine function in sedentary male and female
rats, to exclude the response to exercise stress.

MATERIALS AND METHODS

Animal treatment

Ten male and ten female adlut Sprague-Dawley rats (150 g) were divided into
two groups of five animals. One group was administered orally fluoxymesterone
(Sigma) (2mg/Kg body weight) for 5 days/week. The other one was the control

group. Animals were fed with standard chow and free access to water. After 5 weeks of treatment, animals were fasted overnight and blood was collected by cardiac punture, under ether anesthesia. Immediately, adrenal glands were excised, trimmed of fat, weighed, frozen in liquid nitrogen and stored at -70ºC until use.

Serum and tissue determinations
Serum corticosteroids were measured by a competitive protein binding assay (ref. 5), after previous extraction with dichloromethane.

Serum HDL-Ch, after precipitation with phosphotungstic acid and Mg^{++}, and serum total cholesterol were estimated enzymatically (CHOP-PAP method, Boehringer-Mannheim).

Adrenal free and esterified cholesterol were mesured by the same enzymatic method.

Analysis of data
In these experiments mean values of data were compared with the unpaired Student's t-test (two-tailed).

RESULTS AND DISCUSSION

The treatment of sedentary male and female rats with the anabolizing androgen fluoxymesterone for a five weeks period did not produce any significant increase in the rat body weight. The adrenal glands of treated female rats were decreased in weight when compared with controls. However, the adrenal glands of control and treated male rats did not show any differences (Table 1).

TABLE 1. Variations of adrenal gland weight and serum corticoids levels after fluoxymesterone administration.

	Adrenal weight/body weight (mg/g)	Corticoids (μg/dl)
Male		
Control	0.130+0.006	28.43+1.50
Treated	0.136+0.016	35.93+5.87
P value	N.S.	N.S.
Female		
Control	0.248+0.017	31.28+7.20
Treated	0.181+0.033	14.25+4.58
P value	< 0.01	< 0.01

Mean values + S.D., N.S. = no significant.

Competitive protein binding assays showed that after fluoxymesterone administration, serum corticoid concentrations were reduced by about 45% in females, whereas a small increase (no significant) was observed in male rats (Table 1). Since plasma cholesterol is the main source of substrate for corticoids biosynthesis, we determined the total cholesterol and HDL-cholesterol levels in serum of control and treated animals. The results are shown in Fig. 1. Serum total cholesterol concentrations did not change in males after fluoxymesterone treatment, but a significant decrease was seen in female treated rats. Only this latter group presented alterations in the cholesterol fraction bound to high density lipoproteins. Most of the studies in humans show that the treatment with anabolic steroids leads to a reduction in HDL-cholesterol levels, mainly due to an enhancement of hepatic lipase activity, key enzyme in the regulation of HDL catabolism (ref. 6). A similar decrease in serum HDL-cholesterol concentrations and an impairment of apo A-I synthesis have been found in men and postmenopausal women treated with stanozolol (ref. 7). Analogous mechanisms could mediate the action of fluoxymesterone on HDL-cholesterol levels in female rats. The explanation of the absence of significant alterations in male rats will require further studies.

The reduction in HDL-cholesterol concentrations could involve a decrease in the cholesterol delivery to the adrenal gland, and consequently, a minor sub-

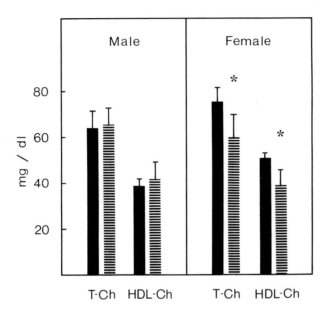

Fig. 1. Serum total cholesterol and HDL-cholesterol concentrations in control (black bar) and fluoxymesterone treated rats (stripped bar). Data are mean±S.D. (*) P≤0.05.

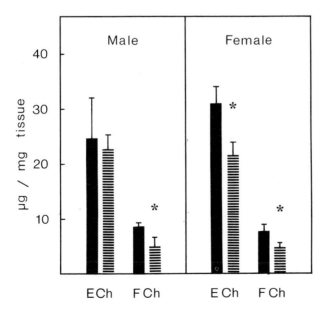

Fig. 2. Esterified and free cholesterol content in adrenal gland of control (black bar) and fluoxymesterone treated rats (stripped bar). Data are mean±S.D. (*) P≤0.05.

strate availability for adrenal steroidogenesis. So, we studied the adrenal free and esterified cholesterol content. Figure 2 shows that there was a significant reduction in cholesterol stores only in female treated rats. Interestingly, the percentage of reduction in adrenal cholesteryl esters shows a good correlation with that of serum HDL-cholesterol. Studies with drugs such as ethinyl estradiol and 4-aminopyrazolopyrimidine which provoke a profound hypocholesterolemia demonstrate a parallel depletion of cholesterol stores in adrenal gland that has a remarkable effect on adrenal steroidogenesis (ref. 8-9) Our data agree with these results, although the reduction observed in serum HDL-cholesterol and adrenal esterified cholesterol levels in female treated rats is not enough to explain the marked decrease in circulating corticoids.

On the other hand, long-term testosterone administration provokes an atrophy of zona fasciculata cells in rat adrenal glands and an inhibition of $\triangle$5-3 β-hydroxysteroid dehydrogenase and 11 β-hydroxylase activities with a correlated fall in plasma concentration of corticosterone (ref. 3). Thus, it would be possible that fluoxymesterone exerted a direct effect on the adrenal gland steroidogenesis, interacting with cytochromes P-450 involved in the hydroxylation reactions.

In conclusion, fluoxymesterone induces different effects in dependence of the sex. The decrease in circulating corticoids observed in females may be partly due to the reduction in cholesterol stores although other direct mechanisms on adrenal steroidogenesis, as well as an accelerated plasma clearance and an action on the hypothalamo-hypophyseal axis could be involved.

Acknowledgments: Supported by grants from Consejo Superior de Deportes and - from CAYCIT PR84-0506-C02-02.

REFERENCES

1. K. Kuoppasalmi and H. Adlercreutz, Exercise Endocrinology, p. 65. Walter de Gruyter. Berlin. New York (1985).
2. H. Adlercreutz, M. Härkönen, K. Kuoppasalmi, H. Näveri, I. Huhtaniemi, H. Tikkanen, K. Remes, A. Dessypris and J. Karvonen Int. J. Sports Med. 7, 27-28 (1986).
3. G. Mazzocchi, L.K. Malendowicz, C. Robba, P. Rebuffat, G. Gottardo, V. Meneghelli and G. G. Nussdorfer, J. Submicrosc. Cytol. 15, 991-1005 (1983).
4. M. Alen, M. Reinilä and R. Vihko, Med. Sci. Sports and Exer. 17, 354-359 (1985).
5. B.E.P. Murphy, J. Clin. Endocr. Metab. 27, 973-990 (1967).
6. M.J. Tikkanen and E.A. Nikkilä, Am. Heart J. 113, 562-567 (1987).
7. S.M. Haffner, R.S. Kushwaha, D.M. Foster, D. Applebaum-Bowden and W.R. Hazzard Metabolism 32, 413-420 (1983).
8. M.M. Magalhaes, M.C. Magalhaes, M.L. Gomes, C. Hipólito-Reis and T.A. Serra Europ. J. Cell Biol. 43, 247-252 (1987).
9. P.I. Brecher and Y. Hyun, Endocrinology 102, 1404-1408 (1978).

Open forum

HEALTH RISKS OF DOPING IN COMPETITIVE ATHLETICS

Open Forum Discussion prepared by John Savory

Panel Members:
A.Ljungquist (Chairman), R. Hamp, L. Josefsson, M. Lubran,
S.D. Vesselinovitch

The Chairman proposed that the main focus of the discussion should center on the health risks of steroid use. Many athletics will risk the consequences of being caught for steroid use, and would continue this type of doping as long as their health is not affected.

The Dutch Sports Federation performed a survey using a questionnaire; the majority of athletes responding did not believe there were health risks of steroid use. Also, they thought that the chance of being detected was minimal.

There are a serious lack of follow-up studies on athletes who have taken steroids which now make it difficult to truly assess health risks. No studies have been published or are underway largely because long term, high dose administration of steroids is considered unethical. Whenever an athlete is informed of potential health risks, often the reply is "where are the facts confirming such risks."

All studies are on relatively short term effects of steroid use. Major effects are hormonal, cardiovascular, liver, behavioral and possibly immunological. The discussion was directed by the Chairman to address these major effects.

1. Hormonal effects
   Luteinizing hormone is depressed resulting in a depression of spermio-genesis in males and causing a virilizing effect in females. Obvious dangers are effects on the reproductive system. One serious aspect of the problem is that many of the adverse effects are irreversible. Acne is common and although it will clear up following discontinuation of steroid use, unattractive scarring is an unpleasant after effect.

   The discussion deviated somewhat from doping in athletics to considera-tion of the proposed use of nandrolone as a male contraceptive. Here the use would be continuous rather than pulsatile as seen athletes. Which of these two regimens might produce the greatest health risks. However, it was considered unlikely that nandrolone would be approved for use by agencies such as the Federal Drug Administration.

   Anabolic steroid treatment has been used for infertility problems since when treatment is stopped there is an overshoot of the testosterone production. For this effect oligopeptides also are administered.

   One major consideration is the administration of steroids and peptide hormones particularly human growth hormone (HGH) to young athletes (10-14 years). There are potential dangers to the permanent good health of these individuals. Young athlete hopefuls (12-15 years) in high jump and tennis may increase their height 5-12 cm using HGH. The long term sequelae are not known. The use of HGH in adults probably is not a serious problem since enhancement of performance has not been established. Any perceived benefit in the adult is considered to result from the placebo effect. Also the immense cost of HGH ($65,000/year) even when produced by recombinant DNA technology, precludes its widespread use. Strong arguments were made that HGH use is not a problem.

Again the question of testing vs education as a means of controlling doping in athletics, was presented. Both means of control are probably needed.

2. Cardiovascular effects
One dramatic effect of anabolic steroid use is the rapid decline of HDL cholesterol concentration. This decline takes place in a few days and can be as great as 50%. A concomitant decrease in apolipoprotein A1 also occurs. Since low HDL cholesterol values have been shown by several epidemiological studies to be a risk factor indicator for coronary heart disease, serious consideration is being given to anabolic steroid use also increasing this risk. Much work is needed in this area and will involve studies on the basic mechanisms of lipid metabolism using modern techniques of molecular biology. The flurry of activity on anabolic steroids and blood lipid abnormalities attests to the potential import- ance of this effect although these changes are well-documented, the exact mechanism at the molecular level is uncertain.

Finally, cardiomyopathy is common in athletes but firm evidence of a link to anabolic steroid use, is lacking. It was suggested however, that cardiomyopathy is the end stage of many initiators, one of which may be anabolic steroids.

3. Hepatic disease
The effects of anabolic steroids on the liver is the longest and most thoroughly investigated. The main problem with the data is that steroids were used to treat people with other diseases. The main question here is that of the possible carcinogenesic effect of anabolic steroids. Studies on rats indicate that anabolic steroids are promoters rather than initiators of liver tumors. The age and sex of the subject is probably of considerable importance since in the experimental rat model, only the young animals develop tumors. Studies on humans are difficult due to the complex dosage regimens which are part of the doping program of many athletes and now only restrospective studies are possible.

The use of alphafetoprotein to monitor possible hepatic malignancy, was discussed but with no definitive conclusions as to its real value.

4. Behavioral effects
Of all adverse side effects of anabolic steroid use, behavioral effects could possibly be the most serious. There is a well documented pharmacological background for these androgenic effects. The Chairman stated that he would invariably detect a anabolic steroid user by behavioral characteristics. Aggression and depression and even suicide are not uncommon in athletes, particularly steroid users. The behavioral effects of these steroids might be potentiated by alcohol consumption. However one cannot yet determine whether a certain personality leads to anabolic steroid use, or whether such use affects the behavior.

5. General considerations
Effects of steroids on immune competence have received some attention but there are no conclusive data.

The question was raised as to the administration of anabolic steroids under medical supervision in order to minimize adverse effects resulting from aseptic technique, shared syringes and black market drugs purity. Such an approach was strongly condemned mainly as being a violation of the Hippocratic Oath.

Finally the group endorsed the American College of Sports Medicine's statement that "there probably are some dangers of anabolic steroid use."

PLANNED "EEC" - RECOMMENDATIONS

2.7.   CRITERIA FOR THE IDENTIFICATION OF AN ANALYTE BY GC-MS

2.7.1.   GC criteria

2.7.1.1. An internal standard should be used if a material suitable for this purpose is available. It should preferably be a stable isotope labelled form of the analyte.

2.7.1.2. The ratio of the retention time of the analyte on GC to that of the internal standard, i.e. the relative retention time of the analyte, should be the same as that of the standard analyte, within a margin of at least 0.5%.

2.7.1.3. If requirement 2.7.1.2. is not fulfilled, or if no internal standard is used, then identification of the analyte must be proved by using co-chromatography.

2.7.1.4. In the case of co-chromatography, the retention time of the analyte added to the sample must coincide with the retention time of the analyte already present in the sample.

2.7.2.   Criteria for GC-LRMS

2.7.2.1. The intensities of at least four diagnostic ions must be measured. If the compound does not yield four diagnostic ions under domestic use, then identification of the analyte should be based on the results of at least two independent GC-LRMS methods with different derivatives and/or ionization techniques, each producing two or three diagnostic ions.

2.7.2.2. The molecular ion should preferably be one of the four diagnostic ions selected.

2.7.2.3. The relative abundancies of all diagnostic ions monitored from the analyte should match those of the standard analyte.

2.7.2.4. The relative intensities of the diagnostic ions detected, expressed as a percentage of the intensity of the base peak, must be the same as those for the standard analyte within a margin of $\pm$ 10% (EI mode) or $\pm$ 20% (CI mode).

Index